# "I'm A Patient, Too"

# "I'm A Patient, Too"

## CanSurmount: THE DYNAMIC SUPPORT PROGRAM FOR CANCER PATIENTS AND THEIR FAMILIES

by
**Albert Fay Hill**

with
Paul K. Hamilton, Jr., M.D.
and
Lynn Ringer

EDITED BY NANCY VANDEMOER HILL

NICK LYONS BOOKS

TO

## The CanSurmount Family

EVERYWHERE

Printed in the United States of America

Typeset by Fisher Composition Inc.

10 9 8 7 6 5 4 3 2 1 ·

The excerpt from *The Natural Mind* by Andrew Weil is reprinted by
permission of Houghton Mifflin Company. Copyright © 1972 by
Andrew Weil.

The excerpt from *Out of Solitude* by Henri J.M. Nouwen, copyright
1974 by Ave Maria Press, is used by permission of the publisher. All
rights reserved.

The poem on page 21 is from *Markings* by Dag Hammarskjold.
Translated by Leif Sjoberg and W.H. Auden. Translation copyright
© 1964 by Alfred A. Knopf, Inc., and Faber and Faber, Ltd. Reprinted
by permission of the publisher.

Quotations from Lewis Thomas are from *The Youngest Science*, by Lewis
Thomas. Copyright © 1983 by Lewis Thomas. Reprinted by permission
of Viking Penguin, Inc.

Library of Congress Cataloging in Publication Data

Hill, Albert Fay.
    I'm a patient, too: Cansuurmount.

    1. Cancer—Patients—Rehabilitation. 2. Self-help
groups. 3. CanSurmount (Organization)). I. Hamilton,
Paul K. II. Ringer, Lynn. III. Hill, Nancy Vandermoer.
IV. CanSurmount (Organization)) V. Title. [DNLM:
1. Medical Oncology—Personal narratives. 3. Social Environment—
personal narratives. QZ 201 H645i]
RC262.H56  1986     362.1'96994'00973     86-18555
ISBN 0-941130-22-3

# Contents

# Authors' Notes

*LYNN RINGER:*    Being a cancer patient changed my life. It was a remarkable learning experience. Patients and families do reach out to one another, perhaps because of an organization . . . or perhaps just because. A network of friendship and strength exists. It only needs to be utilized.

My deepest appreciation goes to my family and close friends who have shared their love and strength with me.

I am indebted to Paul Hamilton for his vision and unending support, and to Fay Hill for his creation of this book.

I am thankful to have known the pioneer volunteers, Sarah Beaghler, Mary Jane Wides and Sally Thomlinson. I am especially thankful for the many outstanding volunteers who followed. Unfortunately, they are too numerous to be named. Their willingness to be involved with the CanSurmount program enabled them to grow and others to be helped. I am grateful for the help of Joan Gilbert, my co-coordinator in early times. It was a pleasure and a privilege to work with her.

Special thanks go to:

The pioneer CanSurmount coordinators.

The early CanSurmount board members for their guidance.

The hospital and clinic staffs who dared to use us.

The American Cancer Society staff who appreciated our vision and helped to make CanSurmount widely available for others.

*PAUL HAMILTON:*    Since 1974 the spirit of CanSurmount has been created by patients, family members and health professionals. This spirit movement has had a tremendous impact on my personal and professional life, and has led to a community of healing.

I am indebted to each of the many members of this community. I am especially indebted to my family. My wife, Anne, has been with me through the valleys and over the peaks of CanSurmount, and she organized and coordinated the first CanSurmount cadre of non-patient volunteers in 1977.

My son, Cap, was editor of the CanSurmount Press for over a year in its early days, and has continued to contribute articles. He also coordinated and arranged the Tuesday evening musicales for patients and families.

My daughter, Melissa, invested much time, patience and diplomacy in coordinating the many events of the tenth anniversary celebration during the summer of 1983.

My son, Skip, and his wife, Ruthie, have been very supportive. Their support was especially symbolized when, with their mountain climbing expertise, they put in a fixed rope on the last 200 feet of CanSurmount Peak. This enabled all of us to ascend to the top with greater security.

There is an appropriate human symbol that embodies the spirit of CanSurmount: it is Lynn Ringer. Her devotion, commitment, sensitivity and caring has brought CanSurmount to where it is today.

I am especially grateful to my former associates who permitted CanSurmount to be born and nurtured it through its infancy and childhood.

Robert F. Berris, M.D. deserves special thanks for his work in organizing and giving leadership to the program at Rose Medical Center, Denver.

David H. Garfield, M.D. gave leadership and nurture to the program at St. Luke's Hospital, Denver.

Kyle M. Fink, M.D. was the medical advisor of the CanSurmount program at Mercy Medical Center.

Marvin Burnett, M.D. has been a constant supporter and advisor to CanSurmount at Presbyterian Medical Center.

I especially want to express gratitude to George H. Curfman, Jr., M.D. who gave his wisdom and guidance to the program at St. Joseph Hospital from 1977 to 1985 when he retired from practice.

The team responsible for this book represents the three points of the therapeutic triangle: Lynn Ringer, the patient; Fay Hill, the family member; and I, the physician. To my knowledge this is the first time cancer has been addressed from all three perspectives. The triangle has become a circle. We three together compose a "circle of caring."

Teilhard de Chardin said, "Some day after mastering the winds, the waves, the tides and gravity, we shall harness from God the energies of love and then, for the second time in the history of the world, man shall have discovered fire."

*FAY HILL:* When I asked the doctors, nurses, patients, volunteers and family members to share with me their feelings and thoughts about the cancer experience and about CanSurmount, I promised I would not cause embarrassment by quoting them directly. Therefore, I have used fictitious names (or none) when quotes express intense feelings or thoughts critical of others. But I have retained actual names where the record requires it or where it can do no harm.

It is impossible to thank sufficiently the many people who participated in the creation of this book. But some were so gracious and generous with their time they must be listed. LaMarr Bomareto is assembling material for a book of her own and yet shared much of it with me. Kay Borvansky not only contributed many articulate and helpful thoughts during her interview but also brought her CanSurmount group together for an entire evening of sharing experiences. Bobby Colby permitted me to sit in on several of her training sessions and granted a personal interview as well. Chris Trani and Regina Schmitt, oncology nurses at Presbyterian Medical Center, were more than generous in sharing their concerns about cancer care. I am only echoing the words of their patients when I say that their kindness, sensitivity and intelligence have been invaluable. Presbyterian Medical Center gave much important assistance. This remarkable hospital was not only the cradle of the first CanSurmount group, but also continues to support the entire effort. John Casey, former president of Presbyterian/St. Luke's Health Care Corporation, has been unfailingly generous and helpful. Erroll Biggs, Ph.D., executive director, Presbyterian Medical Center, has gone out of his way so many times to assist CanSurmount that he deserves special thanks. Sister Mary Andrew of St. Joseph Hospital gave early support to CanSurmount, and the hospital she heads continues to provide a home for an important and strong CanSurmount group. Harry Dowson, owner of Empire Oldsmobile, kindly made available an automobile to me to use in pursuing interviews.

# Foreword

Cancer strikes visceral fear into everyone whose life it touches—patients, family and friends. In spite of any rational awareness we may have of progress in its treatment, we hear the diagnosis as, at worst, a sentence to a painful and humiliating death and, at best, a sentence to a life imprisoned by discomfort and fear.

"*I'm A Patient, Too*" is a window into a community of hope—a community that was given form by the marriage of one man's idea, born of frustrated compassion, to one woman's courage, born of experience. After triumphing in a protracted bout with her cancer, Lynn Ringer and her doctor, Paul K. Hamilton, dedicated themselves to helping other cancer patients piece their dreams back together and restore meaning to their lives. The untiring efforts of these two people resulted in an international movement called "CanSurmount."

The story of CanSurmount is a tribute to, and a celebration of, the possible. For CanSurmount restores those dimensions of care which sophisticated technology pre-empts. Sadly, our all-consuming preoccupation with "the Machine" seems to have eclipsed the knowledge that the focus of health care is the whole human being. The true health of an individual is so much more than the sum of his or her functioning organs. The practice of medicine is not a one-dimensional science, bent on prolonging indefinitely the heartbeat of an organism. It is a living art, an art whose subject is first and unforgettably the quality of human life. Technology is only one of the tools available.

Recognizing that the single most dehumanizing impact of

terminal illness is the usurpation of the patient's free will, CanSurmount is, as the authors say, a conspiracy to improve the health care given in the United States and elsewhere. Individuals who have "been there," who themselves have had cancer, now counsel, support and provide information to patients and family members who are in the midst of their own struggle. A significant degree of self-control is given back to the patient. He is given the information and the courage to become the manager of his life and of his illness, and the attending physician acts as advisor. By catalyzing the honest exchange of information between patient and doctor, CanSurmount closes the gap between the two. While retaining the positive contribution of technology to the treatment of cancer, the quality of life and the dignity of the patient are restored to the center of focus.

There is much to be learned from the story of CanSurmount—not only for those in the health care professions, and those who may be dying from or living with a terminal disease—but for every one of us. We are all human, and as Shakespeare said, we all "owe God a death."

Death in America is the last taboo. As a society we have done a fine job of eliminating the presence of death from our daily lives. And I suspect that we have thereby alienated ourselves from our own personal deaths—denied ourselves the insight that it is death that gives life meaning and significance. Stripped of all relative accomplishments, possessions, social prestige . . . life, in and of itself, is a triumph. Lacking that wisdom, we live in fear. We live apart.

One of the hardest times to help each other is in the face of sickness or death. But when we break through the fear of our own death to share the burden of pain caused by the death or illness of a family member, a friend, even a stranger, we stand squarely before the brilliance of life—in all its honesty, with all its paradoxes, touched by its sweet sadness. The strong and the weak become more fully human, and together we dare to hope.

The story of CanSurmount is the universal story about how compassionate people find and fill unmet needs. This book will share a secret with those who read it:

A priest was speaking with God about heaven and hell. "I will show you hell," said God. They went into a room where a pot of delicious beefstew rested on a table around which sat emaciated people, their bodies ravaged with hunger. The people held spoons with long handles which reached into the pot but were too long to get stew into their mouths. Their suffering was terrible.

"Now I will show you heaven," said God, and they went into an identical room with the savory stew on the table—around which sat people with identical spoons and handles. But these were well nourished and joyous. The priest was baffled, until God said, "Quite simply, you see, these people have learned to feed each other." (Amazon legend)

GOVERNOR RICHARD D. LAMM,
*State of Colorado*

# Introduction

CanSurmount is a volunteer health care organization started in Denver's Presbyterian Medical Center in 1973. Begun by Dr. Paul K. Hamilton, Jr. (a Denver oncologist) and Lynn Ringer (a patient), CanSurmount has spread across the United States, to Canada, Australia, New Zealand and is now being established in several European countries. Dr. Hamilton recognized that doctors were frequently too rushed or emotionally unable to deal with the cancer patient's *personal* needs. So he challenged those who had recovered to help fill that gap by listening to and sharing their own experiences with other cancer patients.

This book tells of early resistance to efforts to launch the organization, of encouraging successes and finally of explosive growth. This is *not* a book in which professionals instruct patients how they *ought* to feel. Rather it is the story of how health professionals, patients and their families became a new kind of therapeutic community.

The book has been written for three reasons: first, to pay homage to the compassionate, dedicated and often heroic volunteers who have given so much to help others who suffer from cancer; second, to challenge professionals in health care to provide the kind of warm, human care that was once common, but has been partly lost in the development of high-tech medicine; third, as one more service by CanSurmount volunteers to those who have just discovered they have cancer.

# Part One

Part One

# 1
# In A Nutshell

"Does this mean my cancer has returned?"

Dr. Paul Hamilton looked up from the charts he was examining. Across from him sat a thin, lovely black woman. She was in her early forties. Several months before, a surgeon had found a malignant lump in her right breast and performed a radical mastectomy. When later tests showed that the cancer had spread she was given a course of radiation therapy and referred to Dr. Hamilton for chemotherapy. She responded well to the drugs and returned to work. A few weeks later she developed a low grade temperature. Like many cancer patients, she was so terrified of the implications she did not consult her physician. But this morning, she had collapsed at her desk. Now she was in the office of Hematology-Oncology Associates. Dr. Hamilton had examined her, ordered tests, and was ready to give her the results.

He sighed. The woman was intelligent and educated. She would understand that his words were virtually a death sentence.

Sandra Walters' life had never been easy. She grew up during the civil rights struggle, a victim of prejudice, but fought for an education and did well in her work. Now she would join the hundreds of patients Paul Hamilton had come to consider friends, only to see so many die.

"We'll need a CAT scan to be sure, Sandra, but I'm afraid it has gone to your liver."

Her eyes swam with tears and her voice was husky. "I thought that was it. Is there anything to do now?"

Dr. Hamilton sat forward in his chair. "Yes! We're not giving up. There are other drugs. But first, we'll get you to the hospital for a CAT scan, and to reduce that temperature."

She nodded, tears rolling down her cheeks. "But will it do any good?"

His bushy eyebrows almost covered his blue eyes as he said, "We'll do everything we can, Sandra. We've had good response to a new combination of drugs, and we'll start treatment as soon as you're strong enough." He was telling the truth. The combination had been miraculous—compared to what they had used to fight metastatic breast cancer in the old days. But if the cancer had gone to the liver . . . .

"I'm so weak," she said. "I feel as if I might faint again. And I don't have anyone at home to help me. I suppose I can call my mother, but she's so old." The tears came again. "What am I going to do?"

"We won't send you home from the hospital until you're able to take care of yourself."

He stole a glance at the clock on his desk. Sandra Walters had been an emergency, and he had made room for her in his already crowded schedule. But he knew three other patients were waiting to see him. Each of them was fighting cancer, too—and losing. The nurse would be annoyed that he was taking so long. But he couldn't just cut Sandra off, ignore her fright, tell her to find her own answers.

"Sandra, we're going to do all we can to stop your malignancy. And if we can't, we will at least keep you comfortable. I promise that. But right now, let's get you to the hospital. I'll see if one of the nurses can walk you over."

He left her and went down the hall. Every nurse was frantically busy. He stepped into the office of the CanSurmount volunteer and saw that Mrs. Irene Spofford was on duty. For a moment he hesitated. Irene was one of Denver's prominent socialites, the wife of a wealthy businessman, daughter of one of the city's most distinguished politicians. And she did not look very strong herself. She too was suffering from metastases to the liver. But there was no one else. He said gently, "Irene? I've got a patient in my office who's got to go to the hospital, and she just can't make it alone. She's already fainted once today, and. . . ."

Instantly the woman stood up. "I'll help her, Paul." She was a tall, attractive woman dressed in an expensive wool skirt and cashmere sweater. She followed him back to his office, and, after he introduced them, the two walked out together. Irene had her hand under Sandra's elbow.

Hamilton sat down and checked his calendar. His next patient was Mr. Osborne, acute granulocytic leukemia. After an aggressive course of chemotherapy he had been in remission for three months. This morning he had called to say he had a nose bleed. An ominous sign. The next appointment was Miss Albright. When she was a child her doctor used x-rays to reduce her swollen adenoids. As a result, in her forties she had developed a cancer of the thyroid. And the cancer metastasized. She could not live more than two or three months. The third patient waiting to see him was Mrs. Richardson. A heavy smoker for years, cancer of the larynx. After a laryngectomy she learned to speak by belching air over her vocal cords. But her cancer metastasized to the bones, she was not responding to chemotherapy and she had lost all her hair. He sighed, called the receptionist and told her he was ready for Mr. Osborne.

While he waited, he turned to the window. Irene Spofford and Sandra Walters were just rounding the corner of the building on their way to Presbyterian Hospital across the street. The thin black woman was leaning heavily against the patrician white woman as they slowly walked down the sidewalk. "CanSurmount in a nutshell!" he thought.

For the first time that afternoon he smiled.

# 2
# The Reassuring Touch

The close-up, reassuring, warm touch of the physician, the comfort and concern, the long, leisurely discussions in which everything including the dog can be worked into the conversation, are disappearing from the practice of medicine, and this may turn out to be too great a loss for the doctor as well as for the patient. This uniquely subtle, personal relationship has roots that go back into the beginnings of medicine's history, and needs preserving. To do it right has never been easy; it takes the best of doctors, the best of friends. Once lost, even for as short a time as one generation, it may be too difficult a task to bring it back again.

If I were a medical student or an intern, just getting ready to begin, I would be more worried about this aspect of my future than anything else. I would be apprehensive that my real job, caring for sick people, might soon be taken away, leaving me with the quite different occupation of looking after machines. I would be trying to figure out ways to keep this from happening.

LEWIS THOMAS
*The Youngest Science*

To be told that you have cancer is a devastating experience. You may never have had a sick day in your life, never have seen the inside of a hospital. But now the doctor has a concerned expression on his face and is struggling to tell you something impossible. A bolt of lightning seems to have seared your brain and you

sit paralyzed, unable to speak or even think clearly. *You* have cancer! You! You turn cold all over and fear sets your hands trembling, your stomach constricting. You are so *young!* So healthy!
How could this happen to you? You were so faithful about not
smoking and about jogging daily! Your body has let you down!

The cancer patient knows he may be looking forward to radical surgery. Surgery may be followed by weeks of radiation or chemotherapy. And that may cause him to spend much of the next
few months nauseated, plagued with diarrhea, mouth sores or
other side effects. Because his immune system is under attack, he
may develop opportunistic diseases like shingles. At the very least
his hair will fall out and people will stare at him and cluck sympathetically behind his back. Convalescence will allow him to work
only part time. And there is always the knowledge that more than
half of those who get cancer will die of it.

One cancer patient says that when the doctor told him he
had testicular cancer, he felt as if he were no longer in the room.
His *body* was there, listening to the doctor, nodding politely to
show he understood. But his *spirit* had floated upward, away. Psychologists describe that experience as denial, an attempt by the
stunned psyche to escape the unendurable reality. However, cancer patients soon discover that they cannot deny reality for long.
There are things to be done. A young woman says:

> The doctor came in, sat down and said to me, "It's malignant." My
> husband just wilted, he cried and was so upset. It was just . . . I
> said, "You mean I have *cancer?*" The doctor said, "We'll talk about
> it tomorrow," and got up to leave. I said, "Hey, you can't just drop
> this bombshell and walk out!" He said, "Well, there's nothing more
> I can tell you now. I'll talk to you about it tomorrow."
>
> I had no tears, no emotion. I was a zombie. I remember riding
> home that night. I said to my husband, "We *can't* be upset. We
> have three little children." I remember when we got home calling
> our marriage encounter group at the church to be on the prayer
> chain. I asked for support for my husband, because at that time he
> needed it more than I did.
>
> I had to cold turkey wean our little girl, so that was painful on
> top of the biopsy. I sat down and talked with our children and told
> them I had a really bad sore on my breast, and I was going to have
> to go in the hospital and have it removed. That I was going to be
> away from home for awhile.

Another young woman reacted this way when told she had leukemia:

> I started to plan to die. I worked on the plan. I painted my house.
> Because, you know, my mother always said, "You don't want some
> stranger coming into your house and finding it dirty." And I
> refused to buy clothes. If you're going to die, you don't need
> clothes. I really needed to go to the dentist, but I wouldn't because
> that would be another expense. I spoiled my son because I wanted
> him to remember me as a good mother. And I asked my husband
> for a divorce, because I didn't want to be a financial burden. And I
> didn't want him to be there if I was going to die. I wanted to
> handle it myself.

Most cancer patients need help. They need information about their treatment, they need assistance in planning for the financial strain, and they need help in making arrangements for their own care after hospitalization. Some want to know their prognosis.

But most of all they need *personal* help to deal with their anger, their fear and their despair. After all, most cancer patients have had little to do with the medical establishment. And in many cases they are in for an experience that is exasperating, even shocking. It may be that their only visits to doctors have been for flu vaccination or annual check-ups. They had no need for a personal relationship with a doctor, and may even have preferred a quick, impersonal visit. Older people may remember how the family doctor came with his black bag full of pink pills and magic potions which he instructed their mother to give. They may well remember that "reassuring, warm touch of the physician, the comfort and the concern." And they may believe that now, in this hour of their devastation, they will again be wrapped in that wonderfully warm friendship.

Some are. One lady tells this astonishing story:

> When I was ready to be dismissed, Dr. Murphy said to my
> husband, "Carl, do you think you can handle this by yourself?"
> Carl said he'd always been able to manage anything medical. He
> had to dress my wound when I was operated on before. I couldn't
> even bear to look at it, but *he* did it. Dr. Murphy said, "I'll tell you
> what. We live out in the suburbs, and we've got a big house. My

wife's a nurse. Why don't you both come stay with us for a couple of days?" We said, "No, thanks." But what a wonderful man!

Another cancer patient says,

> I told Charles that regardless of what happens to me, I want him to realize I've had the very finest care that anyone could give. Dr. Payton is a living doll, a fine, compassionate person. A dedicated doctor!

But this is the late twentieth century, and medicine has changed drastically. We live in an era of mechanized medicine. Certainly, the medical system is very, very good at restoring diseased and damaged bodies. Diseases universally fatal only a few decades ago are now easily diagnosed and cured. Even some kinds of cancer can be controlled or cured. But most new cancer patients discover alarming things. They learn that treatment is expensive. People who have never been hospitalized will not believe the costs. They will suddenly understand why the premiums for their medical insurance have increased so. And they find that they are often treated impersonally, both by the doctor and by the hospital. Sometimes the experience is a nightmare.

For many cancer patients the ordeal begins even before they have been diagnosed. A young woman says,

> I had a biopsy and it was nothing. They told me to go away, forget about it, that I was making a lot of fuss. So I did. When the pain began a couple of months later, I didn't even think of cancer. But I was so tired! I went from one doctor to another. They told me I was being a hypochondriac. Finally, I had so much pain in my leg and even in my back I went to an orthopedic out-patient clinic and had an x-ray. I had had x-rays before, but they had not picked it up. This time they put those x-rays on the wall and looked at them and said I had a primary bone tumor in my femur. But then they did more tests and found it was a secondary from a breast tumor.

The complaint of unutterable weariness in the early stages of the disease is common among cancer patients. Patient after patient tells of asking his doctor about the fatigue, of being given tests which revealed nothing. And far too many times the doctor then patronizingly asks if the patient is having trouble with his or her marriage or at work.

Once diagnosed, hospitalized and undergoing treatment many patients find they are treated like diseases, instead of human beings *with* diseases. The young man with testicular cancer quoted above says,

> Medicine is not really on a human level at this point. It seems like you're dealing more with machines, CAT scans, and . . . . Well, that's the feeling you get while you're in the hospital. You're plugged into IVAC, monitored, doling out chemo and medicine. You end up feeling trapped and an object. You lose your identity. A lot of times I thought of myself as a statistic. You know, this world is pretty cold and cruel, even when you're healthy and. . . .

Other patients are not so philosophical—or forgiving. One woman, a nurse, suffering from metastases to the liver and bones said,

> I realize doctors carry a great burden. They're the captains of the ship. But I regret that . . . . In hospitals even the furniture is insulting! The hard benches. Those awful gowns they give you to wear. Then they make rounds and talk above your bed. You're just a case! And another thing is the distance they put between themselves and their patients. They don't even look at the patient! Just look at his bowels, at the chart, even at their watch. It's so insulting to be treated like that. There is *nothing* worse than being treated as less than a human being.

A man who lost his wife to cancer remembers bitterly,

> Something has been lost along the way. There is rarely a doctor who—most doctors just don't get involved on a personal level anymore. In the business of healing, well, healing is touching, holding, loving, caring. But doctors are so impersonal! And hospitals are big and impersonal! When you're so sick, and so scared, you need your doctor to be a friend.

A young Hodgkin's patient still speaks with unconcealed fury of her experience.

In University Hospital I had the feeling I was basically a body with a tag around my toe. I could have been a corpse. In fact, I had the feeling they might have preferred it if I were a corpse. I'd have caused much less trouble if I had not been vocal and alive. They made me feel I'd done something wrong. To be in this particular position. You know?

Dr. Lewis Thomas, former chancellor of Memorial-Sloan Kettering Cancer Center, says with obvious regret:

The longest and most personal conversations held with hospital patients when they come to the hospital are discussions of finances and insurance, engaged in by personnel trained in accountancy, whose scientific instruments are the computers. The hospitalized patient feels, for a time, like a working part of an immense automated apparatus.

However, he rightly adds,

. . . many patients go home speedily, in good health, cured of their diseases.

But there is the rub for the cancer patient. He may *not* go home cured. Or he goes home knowing he will be returning for weeks and even months of radiation or chemotherapy. He may face the prospect of dying in that impersonal, automated machine called the modern hospital. And it is an experience that can cause the strongest of patients to be filled with dread or rage. A young officer tells of his time in a military hospital.

Some of my memories are: I'm out of control! Not only have I been told that I have a terminal illness, but I'm at their mercy. They just do with me as they please.

A sensitive and troubled nurse says, "I believe the big issue is control. We medical people tend to take away too much control from the patient. Physicians take it away, we all do. Give it back to the patients if they want it."

A woman with thyroid cancer reports that her doctor said, "Hey, forget this year. It's going to be a bad one. Your body is mine now! I'll take control this year."

A doctor laments:

> We don't even have a place in our hospital where we can take them
> and sit down and tell them they have cancer! I talked to a man
> tonight at the nurse's station with people within five feet of us
> carrying on fifteen different conversations. I was talking to this man
> about his wife dying of cancer. I had no place else to go. I walked
> all the way down the hall trying to find a place. Hospitals and
> medicine are not set up to deal with emotions.

Most patients adjust and simply endure the situation. They
may be resentful, but are afraid to say anything. Yet it is a rare
cancer patient who does not complain about the "hand on the
doorknob" syndrome that afflicts so many physicians. The doctor
enters the room with a chart, examines the patient, writes on the
chart, walks to the door, puts his hand on the knob, turns and
asks, "Any questions?" If the patient does have some, the doctor
glances at his watch, gives curt or evasive answers, and leaves as
soon as possible. There are other, less obvious expressions of this
syndrome. It may be that the doctor merely says after the examination, as he leaves hurriedly, "Talk to you later!"

A young woman who had to undergo massive surgery the
next day wanted some information from her doctor. She gathered
her legs under her, patted the bed and said, "Sit here." The doctor
said coldly, "I prefer to stand."

The patient remembers,

> When he said that, it was like a sharp cut in the air. My husband
> and I felt as if the wind had been knocked out of us. The doctor
> then stood there for half an hour, answering all my questions, but
> talking fast and sounding like he was out of breath. Was that so
> much for me to ask?

Physicians are usually polite, and their detachment does not
change their dedication to good medical care, but occasionally,
the patient finds worse than detachment. The physician may be
insensitive or even harsh to a person already devastated by having
to deal with a life-threatening disease. One New Jersey man, desperate because his terminally ill wife was in great pain, called her
physician and asked for him to come and "do something." The
man recalls, "That damned doctor *screamed* at me. I don't mean

talked loud, I mean screamed. He said, 'I told you there's no more I can do for her. Stop calling me!'"

A chaplain relates,

> I stood in the hall of Bethel Hospital and saw a physician talking to the wife of a man who was dying in the room. . . . I was so embarrassed! I didn't mean to eavesdrop, but this doctor was shaking his finger in her face and saying, "Hey, if you don't like what I'm doing, get somebody else! In fact, I'm dismissing you as a patient. I am not going to fool with you anymore."

A woman who had to have her eye removed because of melanoma recalls that the physician called her husband into her room for a consultation. Her distraught husband began to ask a lot of questions.

> The doctor said to my husband, "Mr. Meyer, just sit down and shut up and let me tell you what I have to tell you!" I was ready to punch his lights out! I mean, my poor husband is falling apart, and he needs a big mouth like that to tell him off!

Perhaps the ultimate in insensitivity is an experience one woman had with a gynecologist.

> I went as an outpatient, had this little thing removed from my vulva. The gynecologist was an odd man. All the time he was removing it he was telling me he almost had a nervous breakdown because he wasn't a millionaire by the time he was thirty. Then he dropped this little thing in the pan and said, "I'm not concerned about it at all. Go home and don't worry." I didn't hear anything for ten days, so I called him. He said, "Oh yeah, that was a malignant melanoma. You'd better come in for a consultation." I did and he examined me again, then took me back into his office so he could have a cigarette. He said, "If this thing has gotten into the bloodstream, I'll give you three months." Well, with that lunatic and in the condition I was in, I cried a lot.

For as long as there has been health care, some patients have "sworn by" their doctors while others have grumbled that their doctors do not care enough. But clearly something has changed in modern medicine. In former times the physician not only gave medical help but also comfort and friendship. It is that which is different. Dedicated doctors lament the change.

One older surgeon, noted for his kindness as well as his skill, says,

> I came into medicine just prior to World War II. I think the young physician today is . . . well, we fill our medical schools with high tech performers. Phi Beta Kappas. But when I interview young doctors I want to know what kind of *persons* they are, what attitudes they have toward *people*. I look back—my career is about over. And I think of the men who made such an impact on me in medical school. Not just medically, mechanically, but with their *philosophy*. They still stand tall in my memory. I think the physician who doesn't care about people ought to be in a type of work where he doesn't have a patient-care relationship. We have a tremendous responsibility to our patients. Some high performers can't handle that.

Another mature surgeon said sadly, "I'd like to tell medical students to *listen* to their patients instead of being arrogant or pompous. After all, you're not the one who is sick! *Listen* to them!"

Perhaps the saddest comment was made by Dr. Lewis Thomas:

> As a teacher-physician I had thought of medical students as the very top of the line, and I was not prepared for young men and women as excellent as those Davis veterinary students. It saddens me to say so, but their intellectual quality and verve, their curiosity and skepticism, most of all the sheer fun they were having as students, made them a more interesting lot than I had been used to in medical school.
>
> Watching the students and faculty on their rounds was another small shock. The animal clients were not, as I had rather expected, treated as interesting objects or technological problems to be solved. We rounded through the barnyard wards of sick cattle and horses, pens of ailing hogs, sheds containing scores of pet dogs and cats, cages of birds, even two locked wards for monkeys and chimpanzees, and all of these animals were known and recognized as individuals by the scholars and their professors. Moreover, they were handled with as high a level of affection and regard as I could wish for if I were bedded down in any New York City hospital.

How medicine could change from being the most respected of all professions to one which is often bitterly resented, how physicians could come to be thought of as people who are little interested in their patients is one of the frustrating puzzles of our century. The most common explanation given by doctors themselves is that they are too busy to give emotional support. But it seems unlikely that they are as busy as a former generation of physicians. A shot of penicillin or a prescription for one of the sulfa drugs takes care of many of the diseases that once took so much of a doctor's time. Dr. Lewis Thomas says that his father, who practiced medicine around the turn of the century, saw ten patients an hour. Yet doctors of that generation were idolized by their patients.

A young surgeon says candidly, "It's real easy to be an overworked, harassed doctor. The point is that we're not *that* busy, certainly not too busy to deal with the sort of problems we're supposed to deal with. It's just an excuse for not taking the time."

Others suggest that it is not the doctors but the patients who have changed. They are so accustomed to their doctors being able to cure diseases that they are unrealistic in their expectations. They think the doctor should be able to wave a magic wand and cure every ailment, including cancer. But that seems an unlikely explanation, for even doctors who become patients complain about the lack of personal care they receive from their attending physicians.

Whether patients harbor such expectations or not, they can frequently make life miserable for their doctors. An elderly physician says delicately, "Many patients have personalities which make the physician want to treat them like diseases instead of people." Certainly, the flood of lawsuits for alleged malpractice does not make doctors want to get close to their patients. But it seems more likely that the many lawsuits do not so much *cause* indifference by physicians as *express resentment* at the doctor for his indifference.

Perhaps the most plausible explanation is that the doctor doesn't dare let himself become too involved in the pain of his patients. He would go out of his mind if he did. He would "burn out". Clearly many doctors try to detach themselves in order to save their sanity. One young man says, "I have to keep reminding myself that it's the patient who is ill. If I didn't, I'd go crazy." Yet, the ordinary doctor today can save many more patients than a former generation could dream of helping. Even as recently as the 1930's, doctors could only sit with a patient and hold his hand while he struggled with diphtheria or blood poisoning or polio or typhoid. Yet those early doctors who had to watch so many of their patients die were not accused of "decathecting," of detaching themselves from their patients. They were thought of as warm friends who cared, and who could be depended on to be with the patient until the end.

A further explanation is that the doctor is not trained to be supportive of the patient. One physician says, "The student of medicine is so overwhelmed with the amount of material that it consumes every moment of his time. There is just not enough time in four years of medical school, a year of internship and two or three of residency. There's no time left for non-scientific things." There is something pathetic about a physician thinking he has to be *trained* to care about his patient. Cancer patients are facing the greatest and most authentic challenge of life—death itself. They want the physician to acknowledge that.

But whatever the reasons, the void exists and will probably persist. It took years for medicine to lose its human touch, it will likely take longer to regain it.

Efforts are being made to help patients provide for their personal needs. Nurses report that as their hospital's census has fallen, they have been urged to be more caring, more attentive to "consumers"—hoping they will give a good report to neighbors and friends, or use the hospital if they are sick again. In many hospitals today health care costs rise, the number of nurses is reduced and those who remain have little time to visit with patients. It is left to the nurse's aid, the orderly or perhaps the Candy Striper to "be personal."

Sometimes chaplains and social workers, even psychologists are hired to "give comfort." Yet such help doesn't fill the gap. A young man who found he had Hodgkin's disease remembers entering the hospital with his wife:

> We got there about nine o'clock. The first thing that happened was that everyone was very touchy. Touchy-feely. Very demeaning. One nurse came up to my wife and hugged her and said, "Everything is going to be okay." I thought to myself, "How the hell do you know?"

A woman with metastases from a primary breast cancer said,

> The second time I was in the hospital, this man came in to see me.

He was a psychologist or social worker. He tried so hard to be comforting. He held my hand and listened to me so closely. He thought he knew just what to say to comfort me. All he did was make me mad! I didn't need psychotherapy. I have cancer. Finally, this guy said, "You'd feel better if you'd just go ahead and cry." So I looked him in the eye and asked, "How do *you* know? Have *you* ever had cancer?"

And that is the final dimension of the problem. Even the kindest physician, the most caring health professional, cannot speak from experience. Few professionals have felt their mouths go dry and their hands begin to tremble as the physician gives the awful results of a test. They have not awakened from anesthesia and run their hands down the bed clothes to where a leg used to be. They have not wept over the mutilation of what once was a beautiful, feminine body. They have not lain under the eerily humming radiation therapy machine, had chemotherapy dripped into their veins, known what it is like to lose all their hair, felt the despair, the terror, the loneliness of a cancer patient.

# 3
# The Wounded Healer

## Paul Hamilton

On December 23, 1982 weather forecasters in Denver warned residents that Christmas Eve would bring a severe winter storm to Colorado. Just before dawn on the twenty-fourth it began, big, dry snowflakes. Continuing all day the snow destroyed the feasibility of last minute shopping. A driving wind created huge drifts that virtually stopped traffic.

Suburban Aurora declared an emergency early in the day, ordering all but emergency vehicles to stay off the streets. By early afternoon the metropolitan area was buried under a foot and a half of snow, and transportation was impossible. By nightfall more than two feet had fallen, and the winds whipped and drove the snow into monster drifts. People looked out to find the snow depth greater than the height of their fences.

For hospitals the problems were monumental. Nurses, aides, interns—few could make it to the hospital to relieve the day shift. Those on duty worked on and on. Electricity went off and on as power lines were broken by the snow, repaired, broken again. Fortunately, the census for hospitals was low because of the holidays, but most patients were the seriously ill.

One was Jo Bellinghausen, a tall, beautiful woman of unusual intelligence, married to a successful entrepreneur and inventor. A few years before she had gone to her family doctor for a routine checkup. After seeing the results of her blood tests, he sent her to a hematologist. A bone marrow test revealed that she had leukemia. The specialist started her treatment, but Jo had difficulty relating to him. After a few weeks she mentioned to a friend that she wanted to find a different doctor. The friend asked her father, a physician, for the name of a hematologist. He said, "You may not be able to get him, but I think the finest man in this field, anywhere in the world, is a fellow by the name of Paul Hamilton. See if he'll take you on." Within the week Jo Bellinghausen had made the shift. Under Dr. Hamilton's care she fought leukemia for nine years, until finally her disease became resistant to the drugs and began a remorseless advance. Christmas week of 1982 she entered the hospital for the last time. She would die the morning of the twenty-eighth of December.

Her husband, Tom, remembers:

When we put her in the hospital Paul said to me, "You do realize how serious it is this time?" I said, "Yes. And Jo does too." She was the only patient Dr. Hamilton had at Mercy Hospital that Christmas. Our thirtieth wedding anniversary was the twenty-sixth of December.

The snow began the night before Christmas Eve, and I was trying to get the kids in to Denver to see Jo. I had everybody in the world trying to help me get our two girls in, one from Minneapolis, one from Vermont. One of them finally got in the day after Christmas, and the other the next day. Jo passed away the day after that.

Back to the storm. When it hit, I called Jo that evening and told her somehow I'd be there for our Christmas. I live near the foothills, several miles from the hospital. Christmas, I was up at five. The snow on the driveway was four feet deep in places. I have a pick up truck and the day before I had put on snow tires with studs . . . and I have good chains. It was sitting there in the garage if I could only get it out.

My son, John, and his wife, Judy, live up on a mountain eighteen miles out at eighty-six-hundred feet. I got hold of them early, and they said they'd heard the snow plow on the road below them, which is half a mile away. But John said, "I can't get out with my four wheel drive truck or anything else." Because, of course, up there they had even more snow than we did.

I told him I'd try to shovel out my driveway enough to get the truck out.

Well, I got dug out, and about six called Jo. When I told her what the situation was, she urged me not to come. But I said, "Jo, it's Christmas morning! I'm going to try to go up and get John, because he's insisting that he and Judy want to come too. He's going to put Judy on an old toboggan he has and pull her down the mountain with the Christmas presents. I'll meet them at the road." Judy was four months pregnant, I might add.

John made it, the snow almost up to his neck at times. And how I got there I'll never know. I guess the good Lord wanted us to make it. We got the toboggan in the back of the truck and headed for the hospital. We made it about two in the afternoon. Of course, being so late was eating away at me.

When we walked in the room Jo could tell I was fit to be tied. She said, "I told you not to worry. I had company this morning for a couple of hours." I said, "Who in the hell could get here?" I mean, the nurses couldn't even change shifts. Jo said, "Dr. Paul. He came on cross country skis."

Dr. Hamilton gave up most of his Christmas. Because, well, his house to Mercy Hospital must be five miles. And I think he went on to another hospital to see other patients.

Paul Hamilton was born in Birmingham, Alabama, the only son in a pious family that included two older sisters. He graduated from high school in the depth of the great depression. He attended a small Methodist college in his native city. In his senior year Japanese naval aircraft attacked Pearl Harbor and Paul was sorely tempted to give up his dream of becoming a doctor. But he finally joined the V–12 program, was commissioned and sent to medical school. There he met Anne Caywood, a beautiful young nurse and they were married six months later. He graduated in 1946, did a year of civilian internship, and took a residency in pathology at the Naval Medical Center at Bethesda. After his release from the service, he and Anne and their two sons moved to Denver where Paul worked with an older pathologist at Mercy Hospital. Yet he ached to do more with his life than be a pure technologist. Also, he hated the administrative work which is so important in a laboratory.

So Paul stepped from the monastic isolation of the pathology laboratory into the frustrations and pressures of what is surely one of the most difficult specialties. He became, to use Henri Nouwen's expression from his book of that name, a "wounded healer."

Hematology deals with blood disorders. Those disorders include leukemia. Oncology, usually practiced in conjunction with hematology, is concerned with the medical treatment of tumors.

When Paul started his practice there were few drugs effective in slowing, much less curing, cancers.

Yet, immediately upon entering the practice of hematology and oncology he found that dealing with patients filled a vacuum that had existed within him. It was exhilarating, and restored some of the love of medicine he had experienced in his internship. Quickly, he built a reputation. One patient says, "I don't know what it is about Paul. Hell, he just walks into the room and you feel better. He's a healer, that's what." An aged man who fought cancer for years says, "He is one person who suffered with me. And he's pulled me through every time." A Chicano suffering from leukemia says, "Dr. Hamilton, he takes care of me. He seems pretty interested in me." A Hodgkin's patient asks, "Is there anyone like Paul Hamilton? Is there another, *anywhere?*"

But for all the rewards his practice provides, it also inflicts wounds. The oncologist deals daily with defeat, pain and death. Few can tolerate that for long. In fact, it is said that the average survival as an oncologist is only ten years. His own patients wonder how Paul Hamilton can endure the pain of watching so many who have become his friends sicken and die. A nurse says, "He's such a deep down caring guy. Great with his patients. But I wonder how he's feeling inside. When Mrs. Logan died. That really devastated him." A patient recovered from Hodgkin's says, "I don't know how P.K. does it. To be as feeling a man as he is, and to take the setbacks he has to take. It's amazing he can keep his composure."

So the "wounded healer" cast about for ways to deal with the pain, typically finding it in more service. Enchanted with Egypt from his navy days, Paul returned through a program of the Presbyterian church in which physicians pay their own way to a foreign country to work at a hospital or clinic for a month giving free medical aid. There he found fulfillment teaching indigenous doctors, and helping the people in that war-torn and impoverished land to deal with their cancers. Some he cured, some he gave longer life, some he merely gave relief from pain. The experience was cathartic, and he found healing for himself. Later, he repeated the service in Ethiopia, India, Thailand, and again in Egypt.

He also used athletics to dissipate the pressure of his practice. He and his wife, Anne, built a home in the mountains where they spent many happy hours cross-country skiing, hiking, climbing, and playing tennis. He took up biking and jogging.

But however much pleasure Paul took in his family, in athletics and in his service with mission stations, the pain persisted. He plunged deeper and deeper into a search for spiritual meaning. Already a Presbyterian elder, he studied theology, psychology and meditation. He came to recognize and be grateful for the miracle of death as a release to terminal patients. For a time peace returned.

But the demons would not stay away. However much he accepted the fact of death, however much he rose above his own mortality, a little bit of him died every time he lost a patient. The old discouragement came back, the healer's wounds deepened. He spent more and more of his time alone, meditating, grieving that he could not do more for his patients. No philosophical or theological answer was completely satisfying. Why did there have to be such a horror as cancer? Why did God permit it to exist in His universe? Why did He permit it to strike down so many fine people? And why was he, the doctor, able to cure so *few*? Was his life to be one defeat after another? The wounds of the healer threatened to destroy him.

In the battle he fought within himself, Paul Hamilton was at the same time actually breaking a path for doctors of the future. He was seeking a way to bridge the gap between doctor and patient—without losing the undeniable benefits of high tech medicine or destroying the doctor in the process. He had needed all the aspects of his complex personality to survive in oncology. And now, after fifteen years of practicing the brutal specialty, loneliness bore down, and "guilt" for not being able to do more for his patients gnawed at him. He had to find a way to lessen the burden. A friend and patient summed it up:

> I think he risks a lot getting so close to his patients, because they take so much out of him. You're vulnerable when you care. Dr. Hamilton carries a lot of pain around in him.

The question was, how much longer could he carry that pain? What was to become of his life? Like Dag Hammarskjold, whom he often quotes, he felt driven toward some destiny. But what?

*I am being driven forward*
*Into an unknown land.*
*The pass grows steeper.*
*The air colder and sharper.*
*A wind from my unknown goal*
*Stirs the strings*
*Of expectation.*

*Still the question:*
*Shall I ever get there?*
*There where life resounds,*
*A clear pure note*
*In the silence.*

"Markings,"
DAG HAMMARSKJOLD

---

# Lynn Ringer

For a young woman who was to embody a gentle challenge to the medical establishment, Lynn Ringer had an uneventful early life. She was born in 1939, in Fargo, North Dakota, to Scandinavian parents. Her grandparents had emigrated from Sweden and Norway. During World War II Lynn's father entered the service and was eventually transferred to the Pentagon. In Washington, D.C. Lynn started school and her only brother was born. After the war the family moved back to Fargo where Lynn went through high school. She attended the University of North Dakota for three years, majoring in chemistry. When her parents moved to Omaha, she followed, enrolled at the University of Nebraska and obtained her degree.

The skinny little girl with the huge blue eyes had become a strikingly beautiful young woman. Still slim, she was now tall and erect in carriage, graceful, walking almost like a ballerina, a serious but pleasant, cheerful person. And her character impressed everyone. For even in those early days there was an innocence, a vulnerability which gave her a quiet charisma. But before she could play the role Destiny had ordained, she would have to live through a long and terrible nightmare.

After a few years as a med tech in Omaha, she moved to Colorado, hoping to spend more time skiing. She first worked at a clinic in Denver, then at the National Center for Atmospheric Research in nearby Boulder. While skiing she met Al Ringer, and in 1965 they were married and settled down in an old house in a residential area of that university city. After four years of marriage, when Lynn was twenty-nine, she and Al began to talk about having a family.

*LYNN RINGER:*   We had gotten a house, and I thought, "Oh boy! It would be nice to have a family, or kind of be around home." We could afford me not working. So in December I quit. In the spring I was doing a lot of house stuff, painting the porch. I had my jeans on, and I remember they felt really tight. You know, like when you eat a big dinner. You feel kind of bloated. I felt that way a lot, but I wasn't eating a lot. I am tall and thin, and I don't usually have a weight problem. And I hadn't gained any weight then. I just felt kind of full. No pain, no nothing. That summer I decided I'd take some classes up at CU. Just for the fun of it. I biked to my abnormal psychology class, with my backpack. The road was sort of uphill and down and then back uphill again. I can remember getting home and just falling into my chair and thinking how tired I was. I had never been sick, never even had my tonsils out, never had *any* humungus health problems. So I didn't think it was anything. I had gone to a gynecologist when we were married, just because it was routine when you get married.

We were thinking about a family. So I was conscious of getting pregnant, and probably conscious of what was happening here [pats stomach]. I was watching for a missed period. There wasn't any. But I didn't have problems like that. Oh, occasionally a little, but it all seemed very normal, you know? I mean, women who go off the pill go through all kinds of odd things. I really dismissed my symptoms to flu or summer or something.

We did a lot of hiking that summer, and I can remember being tired all the time. Since then I've heard many cancer patients describe that same feeling. But nobody else seems to know what it's like. It's just a general, overwhelming weariness that doesn't go away. I forgot how well I had been. When you're not well for awhile, then that's just the way you are. You forget what you used to do, or how you felt in the morning. So I could hardly even compare the way I used to be.

Well, summer went on, and I lost my waistline. The people who lived behind us were a little older than we were, and they were very nice. One day the lady and I were chit-chatting over the fence, and I asked her about her doctor, and she recommended a physician here in Boulder. A GP or maybe internist. Fine. I went to see him, and I remember lying down on the table and saying, 'I feel sort of puffy in here, not really comfortable.' He kind of laughed. I was really thin. My face was thin, my arms were thin, you know? I wasn't really well, but everything in here [pats stomach] was getting fat while the rest of me was getting thin. He said, "Well, honey, you certainly don't have a weight problem."

Anyway, he examined me, and nothing was wrong. I mean, I had barium enemas. X-rays. You name it. Nothing was wrong.

He sent me to a urologist, because he thought maybe it was a bladder problem. Everything was fine. Same thing. Down on the table, they poke around, and if there's nothing gross, there's nothing there.

But I still felt bad, so they sent me to see an allergist. He did skin testing on my arms and all over my back. Those little scratches, you know. I was only allergic to two things, remotely. I really like milk and cheese and all those things, and they thought maybe I was allergic to them. They put me on a liquid diet, juice, one thing and the other. I did exactly what they said, and I kept losing weight. But I got fuller in here.

They did a vaginal exam, which usually would be the clue, but evidently the little tumors in there, however they were situated, weren't big enough to feel manually. And I couldn't feel anything. Again, monthly things were going along as scheduled.

Sometime that fall Al was in New York. He travelled a lot then. Anyway, I woke up in the morning, and I felt bad. I mean, I felt *bad*. I called the doctor and said, "I just feel so tired. I don't know what's wrong, but can I come see you?" He said, "Fine. I'm going to put you in the hospital for a few days, and we'll run those tests again. And watch your diet." That sort of thing.

I got the neighbor to watch the dog and I packed my bag and I walked up to the hospital. I called my brother who was in med school at the University of Nebraska. We're terribly close, and have been for years.

Anyway, it was lonesome. And I was scared. That's when I called him. But I wasn't thinking cancer at all. He came padding down the hall about midnight that night. He had driven all the way from Omaha, knowing Al couldn't be there.

They did all those tests, and they couldn't find a thing. Not a thing. But still I was getting fatter. It wasn't anything that . . . . Well, unless, I sat down and said to myself, "Look at me, there's something wrong," I'd dismiss it too. That happens to patients. I've heard that story over and over again. Nothing is wrong, nobody thinks anything is wrong. But inside you know something *is* wrong.

Sometime after this testing, the doctor called me in for a consultation. I remember sitting in his office feeling so weary, and he said, "Mrs. Ringer, do you suppose you could be having some emotional problems at home?" I went home that night with a prescription for barbituates and, well, Al doesn't know anything about medicine. Neither did I. But Al said, "You mean he gave you something to calm your nerves? And you look like this?" Al would have killed the guy if he'd been there.

I didn't know what to think then. Except that maybe I was having problems getting pregnant and worrying about it so much, it was a false pregnancy or something. And there I was in that psychology class, thinking, "Maybe I'm losing my mind, getting to be a hypochondriac." But I'm not that way.

To make a long story short, we went to Oklahoma to see some of Al's family. It was really hot down there and somehow the heat just got to me and I felt so tired again. I remember resting on the couch and thinking, "I just can't get up today." When we got home Al said, "We've got to do something." He was really worried. But we didn't know where to go.

His old college roommate, Dixie Baines, had gone to med school and was a physician in Denver. We hadn't thought of him, because his specialty was infectious diseases. But by this time my tummy was really pushed out, kind of like I was five months pregnant. Enough so my belly button stood out. And when I'd roll over at night things would go "slosh." It was really weird. I was having a back ache, real low, and diarrhea, and all kinds of things.

Anyway, I went to see Dixie Baines. He took one look at me and asked me a zillion questions. Then he said, "Lynn, I want you in the hospital as soon as possible. I don't know what's wrong, but I am going to have you see a gynecologist for further testing." He called Presbyterian, I came home, packed my bags and went.

Dr. Richard Granberg, a gynecologist, did an exam, and I

about went through the ceiling. This time something hurt! Something had gotten bigger. I could feel it myself, and he could feel it. He talked to Al and Dixie and me and said, "I don't know what's happening in there, but obviously you've got some kind of growth on your ovaries. There's no way to tell what it is unless we open you." There were no CAT scans or ultrasound, or any of that stuff. The only way to find out was to do an exploratory operation.

At that point I couldn't have cared less. It was, "Sure. I don't care what you do. I'll be fine, but I just can't be like this forever." Even then the word "cancer" was never mentioned. Dixie never mentioned it and Dr. Granberg didn't either.

Of course, we called my brother and he came out right away. He didn't mention it either.

So I had surgery within a day. And, what they found was that my ovaries were malignant. And I had about six quarts of fluid in there. That's the way I felt, so full. Then, on that little sack? the omentum or something—that holds everything together? There were these little tumors. They couldn't remove those. And on the liver there were more tumors. I had a tummy full of stuff.

From there it was all an uphill battle.

I was in the recovery room and Dr. Granberg, and, well, I had never had an experience with surgery. I felt as if there were a small plate in here. A real funny sensation. It didn't hurt or anything, but it was tight. I remember a black nurse was bathing me and I'll never forget that experience. She was so kind. She just kept talking, kind of soft. She made me feel so comfortable. She was so soothing. I guess when you've been through some abuse, you have no idea where you are or what's happening. But I thought, "I'm in heaven!" I was just—it was wonderful.

Even then I didn't think I had cancer. And when I had gone into surgery there was not, as far as I can recollect, any mention of a total hysterectomy. You know, "We're going to go in and see what's there, and if something has to be taken out, we'll just have to deal with it." I was too tired to care. I trusted everyone. I figured, whatever they had to do was fine.

But then I saw Dr. Granberg in recovery, and he said, "How're you doing?" or something like that. I said, "What did you do?" He said, "We'll talk about it later." "No, tell me right now what you did." And he said, "We had to do a hysterectomy." I don't remember if he told me why. All I knew was I could never have children. And for me, at that point, I had been kind of programming *family, children*! That just totally blew me over. I remember starting to cry. He said, "Honey, you can still have children." He meant I could adopt, but I couldn't connect all that.

Then I remember going back to a double room where there was another lady, an older woman. They started some kind of chemotherapy on me. Internal catheter or something. It made me terribly ill. And I remember her saying, "Oh, honey! A hysterectomy, that's nothing! You'll be fine in no time." By then I knew there was a malignancy in there. I didn't know what was involved, but just the funny comments people would make were awesome. So when that woman said that, I thought, "Oh, yes it *is* something! I can't have kids. And I'm not just here to have my ovaries removed. I have cancer!" But it was too much to run all that by her, and I was really sick.

I remember physicians coming in with lots of interns and residents. Presbyterian is a teaching hospital. So there'd usually be this little flock following someone around. They'd come in and stand around the foot of the bed, and it would go like this: "This is Lynn Ringer, and she's such and such an age, and so forth." They wouldn't even look at you. They'd go on and on, "This is what she's all about," and they'd come and poke a little bit and then they'd be walking out the door and going through the chart and asking their leader some questions.

I was so violently sick. I threw up everything. Mostly due to the chemotherapy going into the abdominal cavity, I think. And they decided to put down a nasogastric tube; they did it at night. I remember the nurse. Everyone looks so strong as they come down over you, and you feel so passive, like a baby. She just stuck this thing down, and it was really hard, when you're throwing up and all. She was not gentle, and she didn't seem to be very comforting. Not, "It's going to be better, don't worry about this. I'll be careful." She just did it. I got the feeling that a messy task was more inconvenient to handle at night. Night nurses would rather come and flash a flashlight in your face, which they do, and see if you're sleeping, than see if you're having a problem. They're not as active as daytime nurses. She was very unpleasant. I didn't meet any other nurses like that.

Another night there was a young nurse, a pleasant one. I was feeling lumpy about not having children, feeling sorry for myself. Feeling pretty poopy. She was about my age, and she sensed I might like to talk. She said, "I see you have this and that, and how are you feeling about what you have?" So I just started talking, and she listened very nicely. She was off duty, so this was on her time. She didn't tell me that until later in the conversation. Finally, she said, "Lynn, I have severe diabetes and I've had it for a number of years. I am not married, so you see, I don't even have a husband to share these things with. Even if I do marry, it is very unlikely I will be able to have children." She said it in a very gentle way and I just lay there. I thought, "Why are you feeling sorry for yourself? This beautiful young woman doesn't even have as much in her life as I have in mine." I'll never forget her. She just turned me around with those few words. It wasn't, "Look at me!" It was really kind. She left, and I never saw her again.

Al decided I shouldn't be in that double room, because the lady talked a lot and we didn't really have any privacy. So he had me moved to a private room. I think about that time my brother, Steve, had to go back to school. And Al had to work. So he would just come down at night, and he was really wrung out! He looked terrible! I felt so bad I couldn't bolster him. He's very quiet. Doesn't say a lot. We'd hardly see each other, and he'd have to leave. It wasn't until years later that Al and I really talked about my being sick. I don't know if we *ever* really talked about what *he* went through.

I remember one time he came in, and they had the rails up on the bed. I had those tubes in me. But somebody had said, "Don't be afraid to take the railings down and get close." We did. We closed the door and he got into bed with me, just on the covers. But we hadn't held each other for so long! I remember we just cried! It was so hard! It was as if we needed that, but in the hospital there was no time for things like that. I think hospitals should encourage it.

Nobody ever really told me just what my chances were. Although the radiation oncologist gave me some percentages. That was interesting. He came in and sat down in the chair and began to talk. "Well, Lynn, your radiation is probably going to start tomorrow. . . ." But he'd look the other way! He couldn't look at me! He gave me percentages. "In situations like this, eighty percent of the women have a recurrence after da de da. Twenty percent do this," and so forth. There was some teeny percentage who do well. All those numbers are gone from my memory now, but all I could think of then was, "By golly, I'm going to be one of those!" But that was the only positive thing the doctor said. He was real uncomfortable talking to me. Maybe because I was really young. I've told him about this later. He's now a radiation oncologist in Montana. Fred Deigert is his name. He's a wonderful man, just new then, young, having trouble telling me all those awful things.

PAUL HAMILTON: Lynn's diagnosis was devastating to everyone. I saw her after surgery, and nobody could see anything but. . . . We had relatively poor drugs for ovarian cancer at that time, and all we could see was three or maybe six months. It was really depressing. I had so little hope for her I tried not to let it get to me. Not as much as somebody I had more hope for. The ones who have a good remission and then relapse after a short lived one, and go down hill so rapidly, they get to you.

So far as the surgeon could tell, the cancer was only on the surface of the liver, but we couldn't really tell. And Lynn had a lot of fluid in her peritoneal cavity which is always a poor prognostic sign. Six quarts! But the peritoneal cavity can hold a lot of fluid, and the patient still be functional.

LYNN RINGER: Then the radiation started. They kind of whup you down there as soon as you can take it. This is the same for everybody. They started five weeks of treatment from here to here on my body, then five weeks from here to here. I was only in the hospital for ten days, so I took most of the radiation treatments as an outpatient.

We had a little stick shift Corvair. I remember Dr. Granberg saying, "Lynn, you've still got stitches, and with radiation you don't mend as rapidly as you should. Don't go upstairs, don't vacuum, don't drive." Well, Al couldn't get off work to drive me in. For a week my mom drove me. She was able to come help us for awhile. We had friends who would have taken me. But I was reluctant to ask. It was all so awesome! There wasn't a system for cancer patients. No network. I didn't think of asking the American Cancer Society for help. I lived in Boulder, and Denver was thirty miles away, so I thought, "I'll just drive." So I did. In a way, it was my sign of independence. I really liked getting in that car. Not to go to those treatments, of course. But I thought, "I can take care of myself. I can get down there. I can drive this car. I can get stronger this way." It was good for me.

Ultimately, through the department at Pres, I found out that in Boulder there was a little old lady in her eighties with breast cancer, and a Chicano lady with breast cancer too, and they needed rides. So I ended up driving them for their treatments. We all got them on the same days. We'd sometimes get sick on the way home, so we'd just open the door and. . . . We were really good for each other, because we could talk about things that our families couldn't talk about. That was probably the first kind of CanSurmounting that I was exposed to. Just because I needed them, and we were all so different. The Chicano lady could hardly speak English and the older lady was a maiden lady. And she was dying. Of course, I didn't know where I was going.

Anyway, the radiation started. Like everyone else, I sat in the waiting room looking around me. There were some people there who looked terrible. You know they're not going to make it, and then you see other people who look pretty good. And you think, "maybe I'm one of those." Or you're determined that you will be. You're there for ten weeks or longer, so you see a lot of people come and go. After awhile, some of them don't show up anymore. Or they show up on carts. Or in wheel chairs.

Back then, the radiation department at Pres was not as lovely as it is today. You could hear people going, "click, click, click" down the halls for their treatment, and the radiation room was all tiled too. Now they've got carpeted rooms and landscape murals on the wall—not that it makes a lot of difference, but it helps. There were cameras in the waiting room that watched you when you came in and then someone announced, "Mrs. Ringer! Next!" You get up and walk to a dressing room where you change into a gown and pajama bottom. Then a little elevator takes you down to the radiation room which obviously is protected from everybody who is well.

You go in, and it's so cold, and when you're not feeling good anyway . . . . I would always be cold. And they'd get you all squared away. You had those red marks on your skin and you couldn't wash them away. It was just real lonesome. They leave you in there while the machine is going. It made a big noise, that particular machine. You think lots of things while you're under there. You can't help but wonder, and I kept kind of hanging on to the . . . . I visualized myself, because that's the only thing I thought of. And I prayed a lot. I'd say to my cells, "Okay, you good guys, you rally this morning! I'm only under here for five minutes, so give it all you've got!" I had some bit of humor to myself while I was under that thing. I think everybody has little tricks they play on themselves. And somehow it works.

After the radiation, the chemotherapy started. I can't remember if I had an overlap or not. Dr. Hamilton was still in his office on Eighteenth Street. It was a little tiny office. I'd have an injection every day for a week or something like that. I'd skip a couple of weeks and then I'd have an injection every day for a week. There were a couple of oral things too, pills. I'd get really nauseated. I just threw up all over the place. Then, when I wasn't on the drug, I was swell. But the diarrhea! That was bad. They give you stuff to help it, but it doesn't do a lot. That was before marijuana was popular. I don't smoke anything, and I've never smoked marijuana. But I sure would have given it a try. There wasn't anything like that around, however.

I baked Scandinavian Christmas cookies with a friend, and I can remember the smell of all that greasy stuff really got to me. I'd run in the bathroom and throw up, go back in and start cooking again. That's just the way it was. It got to be kind of silly, but I just—I had to live my life.

I didn't expect *not* to do well. Nobody ever told me that I wasn't going to do well. They told my brother at my surgery in October that I would be fortunate to get through Christmas. I didn't hear that until years later. I don't exactly know what a miracle is, but I don't think I really should have made it, for a lot of reasons. The liver involvement was the catch. Usually, that's not a goody.

I remember Dr. Hamilton. If I had a week's worth of injections and one had to be on a Saturday, I'd go up and he'd meet me and give me the injection himself. He did it for other patients too. Maybe all doctors did that. Then, later, nurses got into giving chemotherapy. I don't know. I was impressed though.

Of course my hair started falling out. That was tough. I had real long hair and it all came out. I was bald. It seemed like another insult. That began in January.

Not too long after that, Al had an opportunity to go to Europe. He was a salesman for his company. He had gone once before, and this time was going to Switzerland and Germany. So we said, "Let's do it." We didn't have the money, it was all going to the hospital. "But this may be the last time we get to go." We *thought* that way, but we never really *believed* that way. And then we decided to go to the Virgin Islands after the trip, to get warm and cozy. We'd never gone anyplace like that before.

I told Dr. Hamilton I couldn't have my chemotherapy for awhile, and he gave me a doctor's name in England if I got into trouble. But the thought of going to Europe was wonderful. I think it was the best thing for me. It was a big thing to look forward to, and I wanted to feel good enough to go sightseeing. I was just skin and bones, about a hundred and sixteen pounds. I'm a hundred and thirty-five now. I was really skinny.

While Al was busy, I walked all over creation. It was super. He worked really hard, and we didn't have much time together until we went to the Virgin Islands for a week. We had a great time there, just fooling around.

Then it was back to chemotherapy. It started full blast at that point, and went on for about six months. So it wasn't a really long time, though they had told me it would be indefinite. They didn't know when to stop. Because, from time to time, I had ascites. The fluid would build up, and that was scary. I never knew what it meant. Nobody else did either. It would kind of come and go. Dr. Hamilton kept me on a diuretic for—gosh, a couple of years, I think. After awhile they decided that the little seed tumors precipitated the problem and the radiation aggravated it. But it finally went away. That bloat was a recurring fear. Once you've felt that, you know when it's there. It was scary.

PAUL HAMILTON: At the end of her radiation she was still pretty shaky, and then we started her chemotherapy and continued that for six months. She still, right after surgery, reaccumulated fluid. We were pretty discouraged by that. Then, gradually, over a period of months, the fluid subsided, slowly.

LYNN RINGER: Then things got back to normal. I mean, *normal*! After that first year if I had any chemotherapy, it was just a maintenance sort of thing. I have forgotten a lot of the details. I was seeing Dr. Granberg, Dr. Hamilton, and the radiation people regularly.

During the second year I went in for a routine check-up. I was feeling really good. My hair had grown back, I looked good, and I was doing all the normal things. Then Dr. Hamilton said, "Dick and I have been talking." It seems that studies at the time showed that a second look surgery was warranted with ovarian cancer. They couldn't really see what was going on in there. If we were willing, they could go in and take a look, and if nothing was happening, they wouldn't worry about any more chemotherapy.

Or radiation. But as it was, there wasn't really any way to tell. Except by my saying, "I feel swell."

That was a real blow. It took me so long to recover the first time, and I thought, "Oh my gosh, I don't want that many months out of my life again." But I talked it over with Al, and we finally said, "We don't have that much to lose."

So I had it. And as it turned out, there were no tumors. The ones on the liver were, I guess, just little spots. There was nothing. They didn't find *anything*. It was baffling. And my recovery from that surgery was just like that [snaps fingers]. I was strong, not like the first time. After that there was no indication that further treatment was necessary, so since then I haven't had anything.

I can remember the anesthesiologist for the first surgery who had come in as anesthesiologists do, to interview you before surgery. He was a very young man. I guess he was pretty boggled that it turned out so bad. I mean the prognosis was grim. I was so young and didn't know what was going on, why I was even having surgery. Of course, he didn't keep track of me over those two years. But he was called in to be the anesthesiologist for the second surgery, and he saw my name. So the night or the morning before he came up and said, "Are you the same Lynn Ringer?" I said, "Yes," and I didn't really remember him then. He said, "Well, I am the same man who was in on the surgery a couple of years ago. And I am delighted for you." He went on and on about how my case had affected him, how pleased he was to see a cancer patient do well, and anyway, what he did was come back after the second surgery to share his joy. It was so nice. It was *really* nice.

Other people also remembered things about the case, not about me, particularly, but they, too, were elated. I had been unaware of their involvement. It was nice. And then Dr. Hamilton came in and sat on the radiator and celebrated with me about my cure.

*PAUL HAMILTON:* The practice of oncology is a lonely thing. As I look back on that particular time, maybe I was getting burned out. I needed support. Maybe I was becoming the "wounded healer." It's hard to analyze.

Four or five days after Lynn's second surgery, I was—I like to think of it as celebrating her resurrection. I was sitting on the radiator in her room. I asked her if she had been frightened about this latest surgery. She said she hadn't wanted to have it, but that she wasn't frightened. And she told me a story:

*LYNN RINGER:*   At the first surgery, a couple of nights later, I had been moved to that private room and the guard rails were up on the bed, and I was so cold. I was always freezing in there. The nurses had blanketed me down, and given me an IV of something to put me under. I began to feel wonderful. There was no haze, and I felt warm. I really liked that high. I had not prayed that night. Because, as best I can remember, when Dr. Granberg talked to me in the recovery room, when he was through, I just kind of said, "Thanks a lot, God!" That was it. There was no need to talk to *Him* anymore. I had just had it with Him. I was finished. I was so mad!

Anyway, I was feeling warm and sleepy, and I do remember I was not praying. Whatever was going on in my mind, I was not saying, "Okay, God. . . ." I wasn't really thinking about anything. Then I had this very real sensation. I could draw it if I had to, it was so clear. A pair of hands, like this [cups hands together] held me, and I was like a little doll, all bundled up. The hands were rocking gently. It wasn't Jesus. I didn't see a big beard, and I didn't see any shoulders or anything. But it was something immense. It didn't have to be God. It didn't have to be any person, but it *was*. I had this sensation of absolute. . . .

You know, since then, I read that book about people coming back from the dead. *Life After Life.* People say there are no words to describe, to say what you want to say. It was that way. But it was poignantly clear that I was supremely taken care of. I mean, without a doubt. It wasn't telling me not to worry, but at that moment anyway—it was just immense. Something was Okay. And, well, there were no conditions to it. I mean, no obligation was implied. It was just something caring for me, asking nothing in return.

Well, anyway, that vanished, and I went to sleep. I told Al the next night when he came to see me, and he's the only person I ever told for several years. Then, after the second surgery, I told Dr. Hamilton and later the chaplain, Stu Plummer. They were amazed. I felt kind of foolish about it. It didn't make any sense at all. Logically, I felt it was the hypo.

So, I asked Dr. Hamilton before the second surgery if he would give me the same sedative or whatever that was. I said, you know, "I don't need a lot of pain stuff. But whatever that shot was, or IV, it was wonderful. Would you mind letting me have that, a couple of nights in a row?" He agreed. I got all warm and cozy, and the room was dark and the rails were up and I tried, but it didn't work. I felt woozy and sleepy and I even said, "Okay, I'm ready!" But nothing happened.

My theory is, it wasn't the drug. I'll never know. But I decided it wasn't a "Life After Life" experience. And nobody ever said, "You're going to get well," anything like that. It was just enormous peace. If I were ever dead or dying or on my way, and had that feeling again, I would absolutely go. There is no question in my mind. It was—it—the words we have don't work. I don't remember brightness, the way other people do. Just warmth, a supreme Wholeness—like a universal feeling, as if you were so in tune. It sounds really hokey, but . . . I can't explain it. But it was terrific.

*PAUL HAMILTON:*  The way Lynn told that story gave me an insight into her spiritual depths. I saw something in her that really turned a switch. I didn't have any real image about what she could do. I just saw in her a person who could be supportive to me. In, I guess, just sharing the loneliness. I had been thinking about an idea I had, and I asked her if she'd be willing to meet with some other women patients, share experiences, maybe visit with new cancer patients. I didn't even know how they should go about it, but I felt Lynn could work it out. She showed me an article she had clipped out of *Time* Magazine, which she had there in the hospital, about this fellow, Harris. He had a used car business in Los Angeles. When he got carcinoma of the lung and was visited by another patient with the same cancer, he got really enthusiastic and started the CanSurvive program. Lynn had picked up on this, and liked my idea, so we talked a little more about it and she agreed to try.

I have no doubt that without Lynn Ringer, there would have been no CanSurmount. There is something special about her. I've seen her just walk in a room and—something about her, her interest, her presence—brightens the room. Without her, my idea would have been nothing. You know what happened after that day in 1973.

What happened was that an idea took on flesh and became a living, dynamic organization. In the years since that conversation in Lynn

Ringer's hospital room CanSurmount has grown phenomenally. More than five hundred volunteers work in Colorado alone, visiting new cancer patients, giving support and love. CanSurmount is known to have spread to at least twenty eight states, to every province of Canada, to Australia and New Zealand. There are people trying to start groups in Europe and a physician who studied in the United States has taken the idea back to Egypt. Tens of thousands of cancer patients have had their terror and loneliness mitigated by a visit from someone who smiles and says, "I'm a patient, too."

Perhaps most significant, CanSurmount has become a lump of yeast in the health care establishment, gently changing it, or at least challenging it to change. CanSurmount is a kind of conspiracy, a conspiracy of sick people to improve the health care given in our country.

In their epochal study of America's best run companies, *In Search of Excellence*, Peters and Waterman say that one of the marks of a great corporation is that it is clear about what it stands for, and takes the process of value-shaping seriously. That understanding can be passed down through the years to new employees and managers. The authors quote Thomas Watson, Jr.:

> I firmly believe that any organization, in order to survive and achieve success, must have a sound set of beliefs on which it premises all its policies and actions. Next, I believe that the most important single factor in corporate success is faithful adherence to those beliefs. And, finally, I believe if an organization is to meet the challenge of a changing world, it must be prepared to change everything about itself except those beliefs as it moves through corporate life. In other words, the basic philosophy, spirit, and drive of an organization have far more to do with its relative achievements than do technological or economic resources, organizational structure, innovation, and timing. (p. 280, *Search*)

CanSurmount passes this and other tests of a great organization. Although loosely structured, suffering a great deal of turnover in personnel, and having spread incredible distances, it continues to have the same purpose, goals, commitment, accomplishments. Volunteers who have never met Dr. Paul Hamilton or Lynn Ringer all have a firm grasp of what they are doing. *They are serving people*. They have caught the spirit of its two founders. Paul

Hamilton's vision, rising out of his own pain and loneliness, defined it. And Lynn Ringer, having herself fought cancer, gave it form.

---

In 1978 twelve hundred health care professionals gathered in Chicago at the Second National Conference on Human Values and Cancer. The meeting was moderated by LaSalle D. Leffall, Jr., M.D., professor and chairman of the Department of Surgery at Howard University College of Medicine. Introduced by Paul Hamilton, Lynn Ringer stood to speak. In her soft voice she began. Delegates were chatting and reading program notes as is usual in such conferences. But slowly, like goose bumps, silence spread over the huge audience. And for more than thirty minutes the professionals listened in hypnotic silence while the tall, thin young woman told of her experience with cancer, and gave her thoughts on cancer care.

She began, "My story seems so old now—my time with cancer so far away. Those of us patients who do well and seem to cope are often asked to share with others things like our concerns, our frustrations, our scaries, and our dreams. The public often hears or reads about the life and death dreams surrounding cancer patients—the gripping changes or new-found awareness of life that cancer patients may find. Revelations may be given to us—the wild flowers and quiet meadows may be more beautiful in our eyes. Life's annoyances are put into perspective and loved ones are more precious than ever.

"We'd all agree, however, that we'd rather learn and see these things around us without having had cancer. Most of us just muddle along, doing the best we can in spite of the odds. We may not change. We may not be touched. We may not look forward to being healed. We may need your help."

After briefly telling of her own experience with cancer she said, "I am thankful for a God who for whatever reasons decided to let me be around here awhile more.

"We patients will always carry the hidden thought of recurrence and if that happens to me, I'm not sure how it will be. I hope that I've learned something the first time around to help me then. I've surely learned a lot."

"I would like to mention a few suggestions from patients to you as professionals. Perhaps these thoughts will be helpful in reaching the cancer patients you work with.

"Please dare to be vulnerable. We all live in our own little worlds, wearing our masks of everyday. It's much easier to keep our masks on than to remove them and be open to others. Dare to find out about us by asking us relevant questions. Serious questions. Can you be open to asking us such things as, 'Are you able to talk with your husband about your cancer?' 'Do the children understand the seriousness of your disease?' 'Are you afraid of the treatment you're receiving?' 'Are you managing OK with the medical bills?' You may not really want to know all about us and carry our burdens on your shoulders, but if by asking, you can let us unload occasionally, it helps so much. Please don't be afraid to be a friend.

"Often we patients have much bigger concerns worrying us than our cancers. We may have a sick elderly parent at home, a retarded child, or a spouse who has just lost his job. We're not often apt to bring these concerns to you for fear of being a 'bad patient.' We want to be good, quite proper, and not take too much of your busy time. It may sound funny, but it's true. Please know it's a great comfort to know you care about the 'whole of us.'

"If you don't know the answer to our questions, please say so. Somehow, doctors have a way of getting around our difficult questions. We patients often feel uneasy about a fuzzy response and appreciate you more for your honesty. Answers can wait and we'll ask again, if you are open.

"The way you tell patients that they have cancer or further spread of the disease is so important. You may have just come from surgery or a difficult patient problem and are faced with telling one of us that we have another tumor. It's not easy to come from your world into ours, but those moments are scary for us and not often forgotten. Please be gentle.

"It's wonderful when physicians and other professionals are able to suggest other tools to help us cope with our disease. We're usually well aware of surgery, radiation and chemotherapy. I'm thinking of such things as learning how to relax, eating better, and the benefits of exercise. Our faith may be a very important tool in our getting well. These and other kinds of approaches may not help everyone, but they may help many. If we're encouraged and allowed to seek out appropriate alternative aids, it's nice. It's especially nice when our physicians are open to talking about it. If you offer the proper 'tools' to us, we can feel more in control and know what types of treatments and new forms of self-help are credible for us to investigate.

"Please help keep us out of pain. It may be an unwarranted fear for many, but it is a very real fear in most of our minds. Just being able to talk about our pain, whether in our bodies or our minds, can be such a help. Your reassurance of pain control can lift a heavy burden.

"When you're a patient in a hospital bed or in an examination room, you hear a lot. We patients have ears as big as an elephant's. Even if you're down the hallway or through the wall, we'll hear something if you're loud, and of course, we think it's about us. Please be discreet and thoughtful, for we can't help but wonder if you're saying something grim about our prognosis and we feel even more left out.

"Often you come in to see us with an entourage of nurses, residents, therapists, etc. 'Now this is Mrs. Ringer with a history of thus and thus . . .' Flipping through a chart to find our names is no comfort. Talking about and over us as if we're not people but disabled machinery also is not a comfort. It's awfully intimidating to be lying there in a cotton gown you can see through and just be talked about all over your head. Let us feel that we're part of the discussion, too. I know that's hard to do when you're teaching others, but we so appreciate participating in our own little way.

"Our families need your attention. They're often considered tolerated visitors in the hospital. It's difficult for them to catch you long enough to really find out what's happening to their world, too. You may make rounds early in the morning or at a time when family members can't be there. Interns and residents always seem studiously elusive. It's important for our families to know what's going on with us, and we patients don't always hear or tell it like it is. Please make time for them.

"Most of all, I guess we just ask you to listen—not at the end of the bed, flipping through the chart or standing in the doorway, but look at us and listen. We may not be able to tell you what you really need to know. We may be grouchy or weepy. We may be trying to cope with a stiff upper lip and a thin smile and hope you can hear our faint and fearful words. But if you can listen with your eyes and ears and heart, we'll know. It means so very much.

"We're all here on this earth together, and the best we can do is to care for one another. No matter whether you're a physician, a nurse, or a family member, just be a friend. Your touch, your words, and your caring may be the greatest gift of love that you can give a cancer patient. It's a very special gift and in the midst of life's uncertainties, it's a gift we would cherish."

When she finished, the mesmerized throng sat hushed for a moment, then applauded thunderously. For a long time everyone clapped while Lynn blushed and smiled. Finally, people took their seats again, and Dr. Leffall said softly, "There is an old saying: When the nightingale sings, the other birds in the forest fall silent."

# 4
# The CanSurmount Conspiracy

At first I was reluctant to use the term. I didn't want to sensationalize what was happening, and the word *conspiracy* usually has negative associations. Then I came across a book of spiritual exercises in which the Greek novelist, Nikos Kazantzakis, said he wished to signal his comrades "like conspirators," that they might unite for the sake of the earth. The next day the Los Angeles Times carried an account of Canadian Prime Minister Pierre Trudeau's speech to the United Nations Habitat Conference in Vancouver; Trudeau quoted from a passage in which the French scientist-priest Pierre Teilhard de Chardin urged a "conspiracy of love."

Conspire, in its literal sense, means to "breathe together." It is an intimate joining.

MARILYN FERGUSON
*The Aquarian Conspiracy*

Paul Hamilton's idea was simple. Cancer patients, some cured, some in remission and some still actively fighting the disease, could help new patients by sharing experiences and feelings. The volunteer would introduce herself with, "I'm a patient, too." She would listen, give comfort, and by her presence instill confidence that a person can survive cancer—or at the very least have a good quality of life while living with it. But his idea flew in the face of current medical thinking.

In a talk to the Human Values Conference, Paul Hamilton explained:

> I had begun to question the value of traditional roles both for doctor and patient which have never allowed much room for emotional concerns. I also observed that these time-honored roles were often maintained at the cost of quality care for the patient.
>
> In my role as an oncologist, I've noticed that health care professionals, myself included, often approach the cancer problem with a certain nearsightedness focusing on the disease to the point of neglecting the "whole patient." While the approach has been intended to maintain professional "distance," it often prevents us from observing and dealing with important emotional aspects.
>
> Yet, I doubted that overcoming these limitations of tradition and training would be enough. I came to realize that, with many of my patients, I was restricted because I had never had cancer. I had never faced the threat of death, the threat of disability, the isolation that a cancer patient feels. And without that kind of experience, I found it hard to enable my patients to open up and share their feelings.

This realization led to a new approach. Instead of telling the patient as little as possible about his disease, Paul Hamilton told him as much as he wanted to know. Instead of taking control away from the patient and "managing" the cancer for him, Paul invited the person to manage his own life, even his own medical care, using the oncologist as an advisor. Instead of considering family members inconvenient complications, he involved them in the care. Instead of "de-cathecting" he shared the pain, the cares, the concerns. And instead of telling patients who had undergone surgery or other treatment "not to think about" their illness anymore, he challenged them to return to the world of cancer and help those who were just entering the valley.

What seemed like a simple, innocuous thought had revolutionary implications. It proposed that together with Dr. Hamilton the volunteers tackle a problem nobody else wanted to touch: the emotional needs of patients. It launched a "conspiracy" to change the practice of medicine in the twentieth century, to entice members of the health care fraternity into listening to and caring more about patients.

When Paul shared his idea with Lynn Ringer, she was excited about it. She felt particularly strongly because she had met few other cancer patients her age during her illness. And she didn't know anyone who had survived cancer. Her experience was not unusual. A woman remembers:

> The doctors were telling me they were doing great things with Hodgkin's disease and that there were a lot of people alive and well. But I kept saying, "Show me *one*! Let me talk to one person. Just give me a telephone number."

Not long after Lynn returned home from the hospital, Paul called to say that he had talked to three other patients who had agreed to meet with her: Mary Jane Wide, a lymphoma patient, Sara Beaghler, a Hodgkin's patient, and Sally Thomlinson, who was fighting metastatic breast cancer. His nurse, Beverly Welch, who had worked on the oncology ward in Presbyterian Medical Center, would help.

The group of women met in one of their homes to get further acquainted, and to discuss how they would go about visiting with cancer patients. They sat for a whole afternoon, talking about their own experiences with the disease. (That sharing of stories is still the first thing recruits do in their training.)

Lynn says:

> We wrote down a bunch of rules. Right then. Some didn't hold water once we got into it, but we were trying to get organized. One was that I would not talk to mothers, because I didn't have any children. What would I say to a mother? They assigned them to someone else. And we realized we didn't have any men, so what would we do? We'd just have to punt. Paul'd get us some male volunteers eventually. But we wanted to match up people and volunteers by age and circumstances and things. That didn't work at all. We didn't have enough volunteers.

The beginning was modest—and cautious. Those involved were aware that a misstep could destroy the movement. Doctors are typically jealous of their prerogatives and unwilling to give away any authority. Furthermore, they do not want amateurs giving erroneous information to their patients. Some of Paul's own colleagues in Hematology-Oncology Associates were skeptical about what he was doing. One, who later became a strong supporter of CanSurmount, remembers with wry amusement:

> I was not in the least impressed with Paul's idea when he put it forth, because like many doctors I felt I was doing a good job. I was content to handle everything myself. It took a while for me to see that it could make a difference. We doctors tend to be perfectionist, and perfectionism arises from insecurity. If you're insecure, you can't bear to have anyone infringing on your, what you consider your, area of responsibility. That's some cheap psychoanalysis for you! But I came to recognize that the doctor is just a piece of the medical care team. He may be the boss of it, or like to think so, but he can't do it all.

Despite their moments of despair the volume of work grew, and by November of that first year, 1973, Lynn was working two full days. Paul put her on salary and gave her an office—a room that had been a broom closet. She shared it with a secretary. The room was so tiny that if either moved an arm she jabbed the other with her elbow. But it was a place for Lynn and the volunteers to hang their coats, write notes, receive telephone calls—a place to call their own. Soon Lynn was spending most of her time in that office or calling on patients at the hospital across the street.

As the work load grew, and more and more volunteers visited more and more patients, the screening of volunteers became important. CanSurmount was still on thin ice. Lynn says Paul could sense who would be a good volunteer. Another volunteer agrees: "I think his greatest strength is that he has an eye for recognizing potential in people."

Lynn describes those who made the best volunteers:

> They have a pretty good feeling about themselves and about their cancer. That is not to say they *know* they're going to get well. But they *feel* they're going to get well. You'd probably get a different opinion from everyone you talk to, but I *think* there's some kind of inner knowledge. Of course, some who turned us down when we asked just didn't have the time. They had children at home or were working. And many were frightened. They felt uncomfortable in

wards or rooms. The hospital held hard memories, was a scary place for them.

In those first days, when they were still learning to handle visitations, some volunteers had harrowing experiences. Lynn says:

> One of the volunteers went to call on a lady, and when she told the patient who she was the lady grabbed the sheets and pulled them up over her head, shouting, "Get out, get out!" The volunteer was absolutely undone. We found later that the woman reacted this way to everyone. She was peculiar in the first place, but was also terrified about the cancer.

The volunteers were to encounter more than one patient who refused to face the fact that she had cancer. One volunteer entered a room at the request of the doctor, said, "Hello. I'm a cancer patient, *too*, and . . . ." The patient replied coldly, "Why are you calling on *me*? I don't have cancer."

And since cancer can cause disfigurement, some callers were rocked on their heels by the patients they saw. Shirley Jenkins, one of the early volunteers, now a coordinator at Presbyterian Medical Center, tells this story:

> Once I went to call on a patient. The door was closed. Now, anytime the door is closed we've been instructed not to open it, no matter how well we know the patient, without first checking with the nurse. But I knocked on the door. The patient said, "Who's there?" I said, "Shirley." She said, "Come in."
>
> I walked into something I was not prepared for, and it was difficult for me to handle. This woman had had her eye removed. Due to cancer. Which means instead of an eye there was a big socket. I walked in because she invited me, and she was standing at the sink, irrigating the wound. It took my breath away. She was standing there irrigating this hole in her head. I had never seen anything that looked so horrible. But what do you do? Scream? Run? Throw up?
>
> I went in and she continued to irrigate the socket. I sat in the chair where I hoped I wouldn't have to look at it. But she was talking to me, so I had to look. She finally finished and got up on her bed and folded her legs, waiting for the nurse to come in and check her, make sure she had irrigated the socket correctly and that

it was ready for the bandage. I was dying, but I had to sit there and look at her.

I think I handled it all right, but by the time I left I was so sick I couldn't even find my way to the bathroom.

The next day I asked the nurse about it. She said she was very happy the woman had done that. You see, the woman was testing me, watching to see how I reacted. So when she went home, she'd know how her family would react. And how she'd handle their reaction. A very learning experience.

The volunteers must have been handling such incidents well, for they received more and more referrals. The program was burgeoning. Shortly, there were so many patients to see, so many groups to talk to, that Lynn was working full time. Since virtually all the patients they visited were at Presbyterian Medical Center, Paul asked the administrators to adopt CanSurmount as an official program. Lynn was hired as coordinator. She moved her office to Presbyterian and things developed even more rapidly. In 1974 the volunteers made about eight hundred visits and in 1975 the number was sixteen hundred. By June of 1976 the program at Presbyterian was so strong it had forty-four volunteers, and fifteen physicians requesting that CanSurmount contact their patients. In the first five months of that year fifteen hundred ninety-four visits were made.

It was Paul Hamilton who came up with the name for the fledgling organization. Paul explains:

It is devastating and dehumanizing to be diagnosed as having cancer. The cancer *mounts* within, imposing a loss of control, of self-esteem, and of hope. A sense of helplessness and of impending death fill the patient. Such feelings are frequently all consuming.

When the person encounters another who has been there, the CanSurmount volunteer, that volunteer symbolizes hope and courage, and shows that one can become a victor instead of a victim. A belief system is restored, a spiritual healing occurs. The logos is transformed and the person learns he *can*-surmount.

CanSurmount embodies the image of "one hungry, starving pilgrim showing another starving pilgrim where to find bread."

When the patient is told he has cancer, in a spiritual sense he is excommunicated. The CanSurmount volunteer says to the patient, symbolically, "You are accepted. I invite you to become a member of a new community in CanSurmount where you will find others who can say, 'We have cancer, too,' others who have been excommunicated." In a sense, this excommunication symbolizes death, and membership in the new community symbolizes rebirth.

Other hospitals in the Denver area began to inquire about CanSurmount. After Presbyterian Medical Center, Fitzsimons Army Medical Center was the first to adopt the program, at the instigation of Dr. Nicholas DiBella, chief oncologist. Fitzsimons has a unique problem. The only oncology unit for military personnel in an area comprising several states, its patients are usually far from home. Most stay for prolonged treatment and few can afford to bring their families. While that creates a special need for Can-Surmount it also means a constant struggle to get volunteers. Still, there have always been enough volunteers to visit with patients.

General Rose Memorial Hospital, Swedish Hospital and Porter's Hospital soon had active programs.

About that time Lynn appeared on a television program to tell the story of CanSurmount and that attracted a number of new volunteers. One was courageous and talented LaMarr Bomaretto, who quickly became one of the strongest and most dedicated people in the organization. Lynn describes her as "a super volunteer, a good speaker. She could sell anything." LaMarr, a Hodgkin's and melanoma patient (who, incredibly, later developed chronic lymphocytic leukemia as well), brought more power to CanSurmount. Not only a good visitor, she spoke so effectively she shouldered much of the responsibility for making presentations and helping others organize groups. Eventually she was asked by St. Joseph Hospital to start a CanSurmount program there. With the enthusiastic support of the administration and Dr. George Curfman, an oncologist, LaMarr created one of the best programs to be found anywhere. She is now an employee of St. Joseph Hospital where, in addition to serving as CanSurmount coordinator, she directs other programs for cancer patients. Lynn, LaMarr and the volunteers were busy day and night speaking before church groups, meetings of the American Cancer Society, groups of doctors and nurses, and psychology classes at the University of Denver and the University of Colorado.

Such growth brought an unforeseen crisis. CanSurmount could not handle all the requests for information and assistance in organizing new chapters. Lynn confesses that during those days she was out of the office more than she was in it. Funds were always short. Even to get letters typed or copied, or to get a newsletter mimeographed was more than the organization could handle. So they turned to the Colorado Division of the American Cancer Society for help. Henry Davis of that organization had already attended many of their meetings. The group had so impressed him that through his influence the society asked CanSurmount volunteers to speak at some of their functions. Now that CanSurmount had become so large, it seemed wise to consider becoming a part of the established and well-funded American Cancer Society.

Some of the volunteers were reluctant to join the ACS; they wanted to remain independent. But the difficulties they faced overcame their fears, and in 1976 CanSurmount became an official program of the American Cancer Society and remains so today.

One of the interesting aspects of CanSurmount is that other people were independently coming up with similar ideas. We have seen how CanSurvive actually started first, though it did not last. In Richmond, Virginia, Ann Turnage, wife of a professor in Union Seminary, developed cancer of the colon with metastases to the liver. Miraculously, she recovered completely, and with her husband wrote a book, *More Than You Dare Ask*, about her experience. Then she, too, organized a group to provide support to other cancer patients. She brought health care professionals and patients and clergy together to pursue the idea, and they ended up with something very much like CanSurmount. When they learned of the existence of the Colorado group, they sent observers to one of the workshops, and eventually became an official part of CanSurmount. When Mrs. Turnage and her husband moved to Charlotte, North Carolina, she tried to organize a CanSurmount group there. Because she needed a salary to devote the time required, she asked the local division of the American Cancer Society for help. Refused financial assistance, Anne Turnage organized CANcerCARE, got financing from local churches, and based the new organization there instead of in hospitals. CANcerCARE is virtually identical with CanSurmount—except that it has nothing to do with the American Cancer Society. The rapid emergence of such groups shows how great the need was.

In 1979 the American Cancer Society made a movie about CanSurmount, *Circle of Caring*, for its official fund raising film of 1980.

In Canada a cancer patient, Esther Robbins, worked indefatigably to promote CanSurmount and today there are groups in every province. An Australian, Dr. Fred Gunz, an internationally known hematologist, came to Colorado to study the movement, and founded a chapter in Sydney. CanSurmount is now spreading to other cities on that continent.

Experience has shown that CanSurmount works best when it is hospital based. Usually, the hospital hires a cancer patient to organize and coordinate the volunteers, and if the hospital is large enough, the coordinator is a full time, paid employee. In smaller hospitals the coordinator is a volunteer. All visitors are volunteers. There are, of course, individual variations in each group. St. Joseph Hospital in Denver is Roman Catholic, and its program has a strongly religious aspect. For example, there is an annual retreat for volunteers, patients and families.

In Colorado Springs, Jesse Bischoff worked hard to get CanSurmount accepted at local hospitals. She and her volunteers were so successful that one hospital even made available a house where out-of-town cancer patients can stay with their families while receiving treatment. The house is named after a young man, Steven Jeffrey Stearman, who developed a brain tumor, went into remission and worked as a CanSurmount volunteer. He is remembered as "a skilled, caring, professional—one who had the innate ability to bring to the counseling situation a natural empathy and an even-handed toughness—the perfect blend required of a practitioner working in a difficult craft." When Steven died June 13, 1980 the Stearman family furnished the house in his memory. His mother described the gift as "our way of reaching out to people desperately in need of comfort and friendship; our way of perpetuating Steve's commitment to helping people help themselves."

In small towns CanSurmount is sometimes community based, and the coordinator is a volunteer. An example is Kay Borvansky, who works from her home in Steamboat Springs, Colorado. She receives referrals from nurses or doctors, and sends a volunteer to see patients, many of whom are hospitalized miles away.

But everywhere, CanSurmount has the same spirit, the same philosophy, the same mission. Janet Noble, a Hodgkins patient who lived in Larchmont, N.Y., was told of CanSurmount by friends who had heard Paul and Lynn speak at the Human Values Conference in Chicago. Janet wrote Lynn for information. She says that when she read what Lynn sent her it was exactly what she thought, as if she had written it herself. She quickly started a group in her city. Molly Rich attended a workshop Lynn gave in Denver. Excited about what she learned, she went back to her home in Carlisle, Pennsylvania, and told a friend, Ginny Fickel, about CanSurmount. The two started a dynamic group.

Of course, volunteers in places like Larchmont and Carlisle may never have met Paul or Lynn, but they understand and exemplify the CanSurmount spirit. They, too, provide a fellowship for patients and their families that is comforting and healing. One man who lost his wife to cancer travels all over the United States in the course of his business. He tells of visiting a friend in a hospital in Minnesota. While there he decided to see if the hospital had a CanSurmount group.

> I went to the desk and asked. They said, "Oh yes! It's on the third floor." I went up and found a woman in the office. Beautiful lady, reminded me so much of my wife. I walked in, and she stood up. "Can I help you?" I said, "My name is John Sullivan and I'm from Denver. I just lost my wife, and I'm with CanSurmount." She didn't *say* anything. She just ran across the room and threw her arms around me. Her first question was, "Do you know Dr. Hamilton?" I told her he was my wife's doctor, and she said, "We've never had a chance to meet him. Tell me about him."

It continues to be the policy of CanSurmount to call on a patient only when referred by a doctor, or in rare cases such as Steamboat Springs, a nurse. Volunteers are now usually trained in groups, involving at least three sessions, and they do supervised visitation before being accepted as volunteers. Beulah Joslyn, formerly director of nurses at Presbyterian Medical Center in Denver and a metastatic breast cancer patient herself, has provided valuable insight into the way hospitals are run and how professionals operate. Taught never to give opinions on medical care, the volunteers work closely with nurses and doctors, and share anything they have learned from patients that would be helpful in their care.

In a sense, CanSurmount can be seen as one of several self-help health organizations. There is an organization for ostomy patients, one for patients who have had laryngectomies, and for parents of children with cancer. Reach to Recovery, which assists mastectomy patients, was the first of such groups and still has the most chapters. But after only ten years, CanSurmount volunteers see far more patients than any other organization. And CanSurmount differs from the others. In fact, it is that difference that makes it so powerful a challenge to the health care 'industry.' Paul Hamilton explains:

> The difference between other such self-help organizations and CanSurmount is that the others have a concrete, specific mission. They go in and see the new patient, show him the prosthesis, their own prosthesis, show him exercises to do and leave. It's a one mission thing. Of course, there is *some* of the emotional factor. You can't just say it's cut-and-dried. But in CanSurmount what is important is the continuing relationships, not only with the patient but with the family.
>
> The CanSurmount volunteers and the patients will frequently have multiple contacts. In the first hospitalization, and if the patient returns to the hospital, it's picked up again. CanSurmount is not just a one time meeting. And this is where the really meaningful support comes. Over a period of time. Often the volunteer will become a life long friend of both the patient and the family members.
>
> Usually the volunteer writes a report and the physician gets a copy. The report goes on the chart of the patient, temporarily. But when the patient is discharged, the report is destroyed. Anything significant that comes up in the volunteer's dialogue with the patient is reported to the coordinator. Like: "I'm angry at my doctor. He won't listen to me. He's uncaring." The coordinator speaks to the appropriate person. This has worked out very well. Anything extremely confidential that needs to be reported is not written down.

Lynn tells an amusing story of meeting an experienced and confident executive of another volunteer group in the early days of CanSurmount:

> This group had a really powerful program going at the time, a national program. It had opened a lot of doors for CanSurmount, because it had ACS's blessing. Its volunteers got doctor referrals and worked with surgeons. I remember this lady was quite intimidating. She was older, and a military lady at that. She made me feel about this big! She said, "Well, honey, this is a really nice thing you have

here. But where are your brochures? Your manuals? Are you just using *everybody*? Isn't there any training? This is absurd! It's nice, but you could get into this problem and that problem." She gave me one of her manuals, full of rules about what *not* to do. It said things like, "DON'T sit on the bed. DON'T touch the patient." HORRORS! Of course, we do all those things. I thought, WHOA! We're just the opposite of this. But if it means anything to us, let's do it. We were going on a gut feeling, and they were going on a military manual.

I know now they had to be extremely careful. Because when they started, physicians would never let a patient see another patient. Particularly when they'd been through the same experience. The real concern was that the patient would reveal not only herself but her emotional self, and tell this poor soul what to do or not to do. Meanwhile, the doctor's trying to guide the care of the patient, and this lady's in there muffing it. The group had a lot of reasons for being the way it was. But it turned out to be a very rigid program.

That's all changed now. I don't know if CanSurmount had anything to do with it or not. But we came creeping in with our rather radical approach: "Don't worry about matching." "Use what *feels* right." "Let the patient guide you." "Don't be afraid to get a little touchy-feely." "Don't make just one visit." "If you want to visit in the home, do that too." "Write somebody a note after you've seen them if you want to." "See the family." "Visit with the kids in the waiting room." We didn't have many rules. We just sort of slopped around, for good or bad. That other group has revised its image in the past year or so. It's still a lot more "rulish" than we are, but it's softened up a lot. I think it's much a more meaningful program now.

But there have been changes. Resistance from doctors has lessened somewhat, whether because CanSurmount now has the imprimatur of the American Cancer Society, or simply because it has won its spurs, is impossible to say. A story told by a coordinator on the East Coast illustrates:

At that first meeting we had one funny doctor who sat way over in the corner with his arms folded, and when the time came to react to what we had presented, he said, "I don't want any do-gooders working with my patients." He had a lot of other similar comments. He stalked around that whole evening, saying, "I'm going to wait and see."

Well, the interesting thing was that by the time we got CanSurmount rolling his patients began to ask for us. That was fun, because then he had to call on us for help.

Increasingly, doctors accept CanSurmount. The words of an oncologist sum up the way most feel.

CanSurmount is a useful group. It fills a void that has been present for many years in the services that a physician or a nurse can provide. The volunteers help cancer patients and their families cope with the tremendous strain of leading a life with an advanced cancer. They have provided a type of emotional support and listening ear and time that frequently physicians do not provide.

It must be admitted that resistance has not been totally overcome, particularly in areas where CanSurmount is just being introduced. As one volunteer put it, the professionals feel more at home with volunteer organizations that merely give information and leave the patient to cope with his own emotions. In other words, many physicians feel most at home with programs that treat patients the way they do.

The most consistent resistance to CanSurmount seems to be from surgeons. When asked why, one young surgeon explains,

I don't think it's a matter of being antagonistic. It's a matter of timing. People aren't *against* it. It's just the wrong time. It's kind of an out-patient activity. Probably most valuable for people who have the disease out of control. It's a matter of working it in with all the other things that have to be done. For a staging operation, in our practice the patient would be in the hospital, at the earliest, the night before. We'd be working with him as an out-patient. All kinds of stuff to be done when he gets to the hospital. You know, the tubes and IV's and all that. All the garbage that has got to be done prior to an operation.

When it was pointed out to this genuinely kind surgeon that a cancer patient might find it helpful to see a volunteer *before* surgery, he asked why. It was explained that patients are sometimes dismayed at the thought of losing an eye, a leg, or the use of their vocal cords or their rectums. Talking to someone who had endured such surgery and continued to have a good quality of life could be comforting. The thoughtful surgeon nodded. "Well . . . if it could be worked in, it *could* be helpful. I've never thought of it as a pre-operative . . . . I think the time the patient needs a support group is when he's in the care of an oncologist."

An older surgeon says:

> Patients who are candidates for surgery as far as the treatment of cancer goes are almost to a . . . well, every one of them is in a curative situation. In other words, if a patient is operated on, with a suspected malignancy in her breast, and it turns out to be malignant, most of these patients are considered potentially curable. They have whatever treatment you might favor. I mean, as a surgeon, we do mastectomies, but there are other forms of treatment. At the time they have finished their treatment, there is every reason to think they are cured. And a lot of those patients do not require the extensive support that chemotherapy patients require. In other words, they are anxious to get on with their lives. They don't want to be reminded all the time that they've had cancer and surgery. They want to get back to doing things.

It seems strange that one class of physicians, i.e. surgeons, most often refuses to use CanSurmount volunteers, or is reluctant to do so. But when told of their resistance an oncologist guffaws and says:

> You don't understand the character of surgeons! They tend to believe that their treatment is the be-all and end-all. What do they need CanSurmount for? They've already cut out the cancer! It's a question of mind set.

Another oncologist says with a chuckle:

> That's the surgical mentality. Surgeons don't like to be told that what they did is not going to be . . . that the patient is not cured. Surgeons like to think, "I'm cutting this out, and I don't have to worry about it anymore."

Despite resistance or foot-dragging, CanSurmount has grown immensely. In its first ten years it has progressed from a corner in a broom closet to an international organization. It has won-over many doctors and has found quick and enthusiastic acceptance from most patients.

Perhaps its spirited attitude is best exemplified by the way CanSurmount chose to celebrate its tenth anniversary. Paul Hamilton likes to climb mountains, and he found that a 13,333-foot peak in the Gore Range near his home in Dillon was unnamed. It was merely identified with a number. Thinking how great it would be if the peak were designated "CanSurmount," he approached the Commission of Geographic Names of the U.S. Geological Survey. There he found the same attitude cancer patients meet. The professional, in this case possessive federal bureaucrats, preferred to designate the mountain with a number. The commission refused Paul Hamilton's request.

Undeterred, he challenged Colorado CanSurmount members to join him in climbing the peak and christening it "CanSurmount" themselves—even if the name would be unofficial. On September 11, 1983 more than fifty patients and family members showed up for the climb. There were leukemic patients, patients who had lost testicles, who had fought off melanoma and who had dealt with disfiguring skin cancer. There were volunteers in their twenties and volunteers in their late seventies. Not all made it to the top. But they *tried*. Paul and a few of the stronger ones made it all the way and planted the CanSurmount flag. The Geological Survey may not know it, but that mountain is now CanSurmount. Bureaucrats may be able to prevent the name from appearing on maps, but they can't stop people from *thinking* of it as the mountain which commemorates those who are victors over cancer.

Despite federal bureaucratic intransigence, that peak, "CanSurmount," now belongs to cancer patients everywhere in the world who have fought the disease with courage and dignity. It belongs to all those "conspirators" who object to a cancer patient being treated as if he or she were a number instead of a living, suffering, thinking person with a name.

# Part Two

# 5
# That Lonesome Valley

MR. CAMPBELL:    The last week she slept most of the time.
Almost a coma. I never woke her. When she was awake she was in
pain. Well, one day she suddenly woke up and said, very loudly,
"That's where I've been! That is where I've been!"

I said, "What do you mean?"

She got her eyes focused and said, "Do you remember that old
hymn? 'Jesus walked this lonesome valley?'"

I said, "No."

She went right on, as if she'd hadn't heard me.

"He had to walk it by himself.

Oh, nobody else could walk it for him.

He had to walk it by himself."

That's where I've been! Walking the lonesome valley!"

At first it really hurt my feelings. I mean, I had done everything
I could. I worked all day, took care of the kids, cooked for her, gave
her shots, bathed her, even brought her the bed pan. Her mother
had been there constantly, the kids had been wonderful. But she
was talking about being lonesome.

Then I thought about it and knew she wasn't complaining about
the way we had treated her. She was just telling us what it was like.
And that's about as lonely as you can get—lungs filled with cancer,
bones breaking if you move too quickly, always in pain, knowing
you're going to leave five small children without a mother, never
see them grow up. How much more lonely can you be?

What I wanted to say to her . . . but didn't . . . was that I was
walking a lonesome valley too. The two of us, in parallel valleys,
miles apart, both lonesome.

57

Lonesome. There is probably no single word that so describes the way a cancer patient feels. The very nature of cancer isolates him. Nobody else can feel the pain that is coursing through his body. Nobody else can die for the patient if that is her fate. Nobody else can experience the fear that gnaws at his insides. Nobody else can undergo the surgery or radiation or chemotherapy. Nobody else can walk that valley for the person losing part of her body, she has to walk it by herself.

The most that anyone else can do is *understand*. And that can only be done by another patient. A loving nurse, the kindest doctor cannot really know what it is like to have cancer. One man who underwent radical surgery and months of intensive radiation treatment says:

> It's hard for me to believe the medical profession knows what it feels like. You know? Some of them have suffered too, I suppose. But there's nothing in the world like lying there and them telling you you've got cancer. That gets your attention right now.

To fully understand the explosive growth of CanSurmount one must understand the extraordinary, terrifying loneliness of the cancer patient, and how the volunteer, who has been in that lonesome valley himself, can mitigate it.

This is not to suggest that someone with cancer suffers more than victims of other life-threatening and painful diseases. In fact, many cancer patients would not trade places with them. After a group of CanSurmount volunteers visited a hospital dialysis unit, every one said she would rather have her disease than be hooked up to a machine three times a week.

And one volunteer says:

> I have a friend who had Lou Gehrig's disease. And if you'd shake them up in a sack, I think I'd take cancer. Honestly, Lou Gehrig's disease is dreadful! A virile, vibrant person, dying by the half inch. It was very hard to go see him because he couldn't even manage his own saliva. The muscles were so badly gone. He couldn't . . . his eyelids didn't even work. Dreadful. It's not just cancer patients who suffer.

A Canadian CanSurmount volunteer says,

I feel we are more fortunate than somebody who has a heart attack and is gone. Cancer is a long term kind of thing. You have time to get your act together, to realize what is important. And of course, what is important is your family, your friends, what you're doing with your life.

But even under the best of circumstances it is harrowing to have cancer. And one rarely has cancer under the best of circumstances. It seems always to come at a bad time in one's life, complicating things terribly.

We have already mentioned the expense, the pain, the terror. But worst is the loneliness. And everything associated with cancer contributes to that.

## FEAR

Suddenly a person is removed from the crowd of happy, working, healthy people and is faced with surgery or other forms of painful therapy, and with the possibility of death. A Canadian woman describes her experience.

I chose not to stay in the hospital, so I was at home when the pathology report came back. John, my husband, answered the telephone when the doctor called. He was in the kitchen. I was upstairs in bed. I picked up the phone, too. The doctor said, "The news is very, very bad." John said, "What do you mean? What is happening?" He said, "She has lymphosarcoma." John said, "What is the prognosis?" He said, "It couldn't be worse." John said, "What do you suggest we do at this point?" He said, "Well, let me see. Tomorrow's Good Friday. My office is closed. Give me a call on Tuesday and we'll discuss it." Click. That was my introduction to the world of cancer.

Cancer patients soon learn what it is like to weep. A woman who was the victim of three different, apparently unrelated kinds of cancer says,

Unless you've cried in a hospital bed, you haven't experienced tears rolling into your ears. Most people say tears roll down your cheeks, but cancer patients' tears roll into their ears.

It may distress doctors to see a patient weep, but the fact is the cancer patient has a lot to cry about. Fear is paralyzing, isolating. One young Hodgkin's patient remembers her experience in a large midwestern hospital:

> It was the first time I had faced death. Lying there in bed I could hear people screaming in pain. At night I could hear the bodies being wheeled down the hallway on gurnies—people I had known the day before. They took the bodies out at night. It was all in a real sterile environment, you know. My roommate was really young, probably twelve. She died while I was there. After I got out of the hospital, for a long time, maybe a month, I had this black cloud hovering over my head. It was death. It took me a while to realize that I wasn't dying, but living.

Some patients do not find relief in going home. There is always the spectre of a return of the cancer. A mastectomy patient remembers:

> About ten days after I got home, and the phone calls had tapered off, and people weren't tramping in and out of the house, the gravity of what had happened, that I had cancer, really hit me. I panicked. Night was the worst time for me. It was quiet, I was alone with my thoughts. All I knew was that I had cancer and four or five lymph nodes were involved, which meant the cancer had travelled to a certain extent. I was going to have to go through chemotherapy.

For some cancer patients the fear *never* leaves. Recurrences rob them of any peace of mind. One lady says:

> When I was thirty-seven years old I had a tumor in the salivary gland. It was operated on and everything went well for awhile. Then a tumor showed up in my left lung. I had that removed, and on the two month check-up another one showed up. So they did radiation therapy. About five years after that another tumor turned up in the left lung, which was operated on. Then another five year period went by, before I had a tumor in the right lung. All these were secondary to the primary tumor in the salivary gland. The right lung was radiated. That was last fall. Then, in March of last year I felt a lump in my stomach area and went to the doctor. I

found out it was my kidney. My left kidney was removed. Right now I'm fine. But I've been fighting this battle for seventeen years.

Even with no recurrence there is frequently only a respite from the fear. Every pain, any disturbance of the normal functions of the body recalls it. These false alarms leave cancer patients emotionally exhausted. The experience of one housewife, who had a recurrence after a mastectomy, is typical.

Because I had a low grade fever, they gave me a lot of tests. The doctor was sure it was a return of the cancer. It wasn't until they ran the CAT scan that they found what they thought was the problem. It looked like I had a mass in my right kidney. The doctor called and told me. He said, "We're probably going to have to operate." It turned out be a birth defect. And the fever was due to too much thyroid. A couple of weeks ago he again thought I had a return of the cancer. I had a hot spot on my shoulder. It turned out to be arthritis.

The wife of a cancer patient remembers what it was like for him the first night in the hospital:

They put Tom in a room with another cancer patient, who spent the whole night throwing up. Tom was lying in bed, totally petrified, hearing this man, and saying, "Is this going to be me?" We saw a lot of death there. A lot of pain and suffering too.

A woman who suffered two kinds of cancer tells of her despair when she learned of the second tumor:

It just did away with every bit of hope. I had all these horrible images of doctors cutting on me until I died.

## PAIN

The fear of what is coming is soon justified. Surgery, under the best of circumstances is unpleasant. And for the cancer patient, who often must have masses of tissue removed, it is frequently exceedingly painful. And, as fear isolates the patient, so does pain. A young man who had extensive surgery remembers the experience:

It was really rough when they removed the lymph nodes. An eight hour surgery. It took me a good two years to work that all out. For a long time, if I'd walk over to the park, and I'd glance over and see the towers of the hospital, you know, I'd get the . . . I'd just shudder. Driving by on the street, by almost *any* hospital, from the *outside*, sent chills through me.

A particularly kind and sympathetic volunteer describes the ordeal of one cancer patient she visited:

I remember this darling little Mexican lady. She didn't speak very good English. She would say, "I just scream! I just scream! I told them they couldn't do that to me again." Her hands got so terrible, the veins, they couldn't find anything to put the needle in. She said, "I just scream!" She had to *tell* somebody that. The staff were the ones doing this to her, and she didn't care if she died. They couldn't treat her like that. She couldn't stand any more needles. She just looked upon some of us as, well, she could tell *us* how terrible it was. A nice lady. We cared a lot about her. She taught us a lot.

## TREATMENT

The side effects of vigorous treatment can cause problems which increase one's loneliness. A woman whose husband eventually died of metastasized prostatic cancer tells this story:

The third hot spot really frightened me. It was on a vertebra. I thought, 'Oh! This means paralysis.' He started to become paralyzed. So they rushed him in and gave him large doses of steroids. Plus, super intensive radiation. They saved him from paralysis, but the radiation destroyed some lung tissue. And because of the steroids he picked up staph pneumonia.

One lady reports that chemotherapy gave her distressing mouth sores as well as causing her to throw up and lose her hair. A leukemia patient has dealt with similar sores for more than fifteen years. A young woman whose leg was amputated and who then developed metastases to the lungs said that the vigorous course of chemotherapy seriously distorted her vision.

It is no wonder that despair and loneliness become overwhelming. A young woman who contracted Hodgkin's as a high school student remembers:

> The second operation was bad. They cut around the back to the front, in my belly. I couldn't move the next day. For days after the operation I was so sore, I was bent over, and my stomach just wrenched in pain. I was so depressed and didn't know what was going on. I think the whole idea of the cancer was just coming down on me. I was lying in a hospital bed and couldn't get to sleep that night, and I remember wondering if it was all worth it. I decided to put a pillow over my head. I did. Later I laughed about that.

A man whose young wife died of widespread metastases of breast cancer remembers,

> Toward the end, she suddenly woke up and said, "I took them, *all* of them." I asked what she had taken. She said, "The aspirin! I took them all! I can't stand it anymore!" But the bottle was as full as it had been hours before. She had only dreamed of doing it, maybe wanted to get up the nerve to do it.

## INDIGNITY

Sometimes it is not so much the severity of treatment that isolates the patient as it is the *indignity*, the de-humanizing nature of the treatment. Occasionally, an insensitive doctor, nurse or attendant will contribute to this. A man who took his wife to a hospital in New Jersey for a radical mastectomy remembers:

> That night we went to the hospital. I got somebody to take care of the kids and stayed with her. We couldn't sit in her room because there were people there, visiting the other patients. They were having a party. We wanted to be together, to talk. So we walked down the hall. Back and forth. There was a room there, sort of a wash room with a sink and piles of towels and things. We went in, and I held her in my arms and she cried and I did too. Then a nurse came and was furious that we were in there. She told us we had to leave. So we went back to the room—and the party.

One beautiful young woman reported that severe chemotherapy caused her to lose not only all the hair on her head but her eyelashes, eyebrows, pubic hair, and even the hair in her nose. So her nose dripped all the time, causing her acute embarrassment. A young man undergoing chemotherapy shampooed his hair while taking a shower. To his horror virtually all of it came out on the towel. For many, having to use the bedpan is humiliating.

The mother of a young man who died in his early twenties of a rare cancer of the nerves took him to a famous Southwestern hospital that specialized in cancer. She reports that he said, "I can't stay here, Mom. They're so cold." She adds:

> He got sick and tired of those people who'd never had cancer coming in and telling him they understood how he felt. The patient representatives come in and want to know how you are. And other people. They all say, "I know how you feel." But they don't.

A CanSurmount volunteer remembers one person who fought back against the indignities and humiliations of treatment.

> I liked the old rancher man. I think he came in from Wyoming. He refused to stay in that hospital bed with pajamas on. He got up and dressed every morning. [Laughs] Now, don't you give him credit? I just loved that fellow. He was there a long time too, but up and dressed each day. He would not sit there in that undignified manner!

## DECISIONS

A cancer patient must make decisions, sometimes appallingly difficult ones. And there is nothing so lonely as being the only one in the world who can make them. One man, a former military officer, lost his first wife to cancer. He watched her fight it for years, watched her go through the distressing chemotherapeutic regimen, and vowed that *he* would never endure the rigors of such treatment. He would rather die. But then he, too, got cancer and lay on a hospital bed, listening to his physician tell him the surgery had not been successful and that his body was no longer responding to radiation therapy. The man had to make a choice. He submitted to the chemotherapy he hated. Some patients have to decide if they will permit surgeons to remove a leg, an eye, ovaries or testicles, part of the face. It is a lonesome moment.

Another lonely decision is whether to dismiss a physician whom the patient does not feel is competent or does not like. A woman from the north country remembers the dilemma:

> When I asked the surgeon point blank if he thought this mass in my groin could be malignant, he said, "Oh, I wouldn't be prepared to venture an opinion." He was called out of the room and I turned my chart around. It said in big letters, "Malignancy." Maybe I should have looked elsewhere, found another surgeon. But you are so upset at the time, you don't really think of all the options open to you. I would certainly recommend to other cancer patients that if they have an experience like that, they go to another surgeon.

However, it is sometimes extremely difficult for cancer patients to make a change. A hospital chaplain tells of such a situation.

> A woman from out on the plains, here in Colorado, came in to a meeting, and we were talking about blowing the whistle on a physician, who . . . I can't remember the problem. I said, "Why don't you go home and tell him?" She said, "No!" Jumped right out of her chair. "He might refuse to see me." I said, "What about going to another doctor?" She said, "There *is* no other doctor in my town."

## WORK PROBLEMS

An extremely difficult challenge is how the cancer patient will continue to work. If the person is the chief breadwinner for the family, it is a crucial one. And for most patients, working is important for their psychological welfare. The person who is forced to quit, even temporarily, may feel useless. That can contribute to the discouragement of having cancer. He may sit at home and brood, worrying about his health, his medical expenses and the loss of income. But if he does return to work, he may find a cold welcome. In an October 15, 1984 article, UPI cited a study conducted by Dr. Francis Feldman of the University of Southern California. Dr. Feldman is reported as saying, "Job discrimination by bosses or co-workers awaits 84% of successfully treated cancer patients who return to blue collar jobs and more than half going back to white collar jobs." The discrimination by employers was said to range from demotion and denial of advancement, to forcing the recovered patient to give up group health insurance as the price of keeping the job.

If the patient decides to seek other employment, he soon finds that discrimination is even worse. It is virtually impossible to find a new job. So, many patients do not tell their employers or fellow employees they have been treated for cancer. That exacerbates the patient's loneliness.

Yet returning to work may bring other problems. One woman, a divorcee with a child, remembers:

> I moved into an apartment adjacent to my work so I didn't have far to go. Every day my father would pick me up by the back door at three o'clock and take me home. Every Friday I'd go get my radiation treatment, then over to my internist who would give me iron shots. Then I'd go down and get my chemotherapy. And I'd come home and be in bed from Friday night until Monday morning when I'd get up and come to work. It was a rough program. But I only missed one day in eighteen months.

Sometimes the person returns to work still suffering from the pain caused by surgery. One lovely young woman had a melanoma removed from her leg during her first year of teaching.

> When I first got back, it was hard because I was still in a little bit of pain. Sometimes the tears would come. Then the kids would get tears in their eyes. That just made me really . . . well, it took my tears away.

Many cancer patients have undergone serious surgery which makes it difficult or even impossible to work. One woman had to give up her business.

> I had a flower shop. But as a result of the operation, they removed muscle in my right arm and. . . . People don't realize how much physical work there is to being a florist. There's a lot of lifting, keeping your arms up. I started getting pains and taking Darvon and aspirin and so forth. It was really difficult. And it wasn't economically feasible. I was hiring too much help. I couldn't do it

myself. So I had to sell the shop. That was very painful. It was a really nice shop. There is a lot of happiness in a flower shop.

A young woman who lost a leg had to give up her work and accept social security assistance. Since her leg was amputated at the hip, she is never comfortable sitting. Of course, walking is both painful and slow. But when Congress made cuts in the budget, she was told by the Social Security Administration that her benefits were to be terminated. They expected her to go back to work. She is appealing the decision.

A former Hodgkin's patient and long-time CanSurmount volunteer tells this story:

A woman I worked with for years got cancer. She had a mastectomy, then ovarian cancer. She continued to work as long as she could. She would be sitting in her cubicle talking on the telephone, being herself, but she'd have her head down on the desk, because she did not have the strength to hold it up.

It is not always heroism that keeps the cancer patient working, not always the need to feel useful. Sometimes it is pure necessity.

I have these three children and that kept me going. I had to work forty hours a week. You just can't stop, no matter what. Sometimes I hate the fact that I am a really strong person. Maybe I am too masculine. I wish I had somebody to treat me like a little baby. I guess I'm not the kind of person people feel sorry for. . . . I'm married, you know? But I might as well not be. I mean, I support *him*! (Pause) When I lost my hair my big fear was that somebody at work would see my wig, because I never told anybody at all. It was awful, a sort of nightmare.

## RADICAL SURGERY

Literally any part of the body may be affected by cancer. If surgical removal of that part is required, not only must the patient suffer its loss, he may also be frightening to others. One of the more common such problems is a colostomy, in which the rectum or lower intestine is removed and the patient must defecate into a bag. This may be embarrassing, and may also cause an unpleasant odor which makes people shun the person, deepening his lone-liness. Many cancer patients have had their larynxes removed, so they cannot talk unless they learn to swallow air and belch it over their vocal cords. They may choose to use an electronic device which they hold to their throats, while mouthing words. The result is a tinny sounding monotone, something like a computer talking. Either solution can cause friends, who may find the sound disturbing, to avoid such patients.

Children suffering from retinoblastoma must have the affected eye removed to save their lives. (Enucleation is the technical term.) Occasionally, both eyes must be taken.

For women, breast tumors are among the most common forms of cancer. And while today radical mastectomies (removing the entire breast, the underlying muscle and certain lymph nodes) are rarely done, the entire breast is almost always removed. In addition to the physical aspect, the patient must deal with the emotional shock of losing a breast. A CanSurmount coordinator tells this story:

> This forty year old gal, bless her heart, for the three weeks between the mastectomy and the hysterectomy, wanted to know what she could put in her bra to make the one side look as heavy as the other side. She tried to work in that period, and she stuffed one side of her bra with cotton balls. So here she is working with her hands, and the cotton balls are crawling up her shirt and out her armpit. You know, I came back from seeing her and I cried and cried.

Sometimes the operation is even more serious, damaging one's ability to get through life. The broken hearted mother of a young woman who eventually died of brain cancer told of her daughter's surgery.

> They got what they could of the tumor. But the operation affected the motor part. She was in the hospital a month. Her hand curled, and she had to learn to walk all over again.

One can imagine the loneliness of an attractive girl in her early twenties having to re-learn such simple motor tasks as walking, while others her age were going dancing or rafting on the Colorado River.

Younger, unmarried people have an additional concern.

The only time I broke down was the day they came in and took off the bandage and I saw my leg for the first time. There was this gap in my leg. My first reaction was, "I'm young. I'm not married. Who's going to want me now? I've got this gap in my leg and I've had cancer and . . ."

If the surgery leaves one grotesque, the loneliness can be agonizing. To become the object of horror, to cause others to wince, even turn away, is to be dreadfully isolated. A CanSurmount volunteer tells of one such person whom she called on in a western hospital.

I remember a terrible experience. I was asked to visit a woman who had facial cancer. Most of her face had been destroyed. I was warned in advance. She looked awful. They were doing something with skin grafts, because she had a flap of skin attached under her eye, which was coming from her chest. Well, I was expecting to see something really bad. I was geared up for that. But then she started to talk about her child, a three year old, and about going home. She was worried about how he was going to react to the way she looked. I don't think I will ever get over that. When I left I was a wreck. She was looking to *me*. I mean, here I was presenting myself as someone coming to help, and I didn't have any help for that woman. I felt totally drained and helpless and awful.

## GRIEF FOR FAMILIES

The preceding quote also illustrates one of the most difficult of all the burdens the cancer patient must bear. Knowing that she is causing pain and sorrow to those she loves, she tries to keep a "stiff upper lip," tries not to complain or show emotion. This means further isolation. One young mother who underwent surgery and an aggressive round of chemotherapy for breast cancer tells what it was like.

I buried a lot of my emotions because I had to be strong for my family, my husband. I had to be a fighter. It's just been recently, when I was through chemotherapy, that I could let go.

A mature woman who has fought cancer for more than a decade, enduring several recurrences, says:

The worst time is when I know I have to go back to the hospital for some kind of treatment, and I have to build up my family that I'm going to be okay. I suppose I am trying to persuade myself at the same time.

A charming young woman who is the coordinator of a Can-Surmount group in a small western town says:

My husband was as distraught, probably more so, as I was. I felt a lot of times I was holding him and the rest of my family together. He was afraid he was going to lose me, and we have a very good relationship. You see all these people falling apart in divorce, and we're holding together and what happens? Somebody gets sick and there is the possibility of being separated not because we couldn't get along but because of illness. You know? He was a mess. A real mess.

After that sympathetic remark, she adds, first with a twinkle in her eye and then a catch in her voice,

I always tease my husband. I tell him, "I know you'll find an eighteen year old someplace." But what about my kids? Nobody can really replace your mommy. The little guy, I thought, "Gosh, he'll not even remember who I was."

## GUILT

It may be concern for loved ones which causes what may be the strangest, most devastating and isolating of all emotions within the cancer patient. Many feel a terrible *guilt*, as if *they* were responsible for the disease which is ravaging them and tormenting their families. A woman dying of metastatic breast cancer after a seven year fight knew that her husband was exhausted from trying to work and to care for her, that her children were terrified and that expenses were mounting. One night she took his hand and, weeping, said, "What am I doing to you? And to the children?"

About her treatment in a large hospital a young woman says bitterly, "They made me feel I had done something wrong. To be in this particular position. You know? There was some kind of guilt that I felt about the whole thing."

An elderly woman who had led a salty life endured the loss of an eye because of melanoma. Then she developed a breast tumor and eventually metastases. She sadly reflected on her life as she lay dying in her hospital bed.

This is my third time, and you know how that is! Three times and you're out. But it's time sometime anyway. I'm seventy now. [Long silence] It's like people think you've been bad, that's why you got it. Sometimes *I* think that, though. I think I must have made so many mistakes in my life, done so many bad things, that . . . .

# 6
# No One To Talk To

Not only the patient is affected by his cancer. Many families simply do not know how to deal with the overwhelming shock of having a loved one fall ill. Handling mechanical things like getting the housework done, or working at a second job to cover added expenses is the easier part. It is the emotional aspect that is hardest for family members and friends. Very few will even touch it. As a result, cancer patients often find that nobody wants to talk with them about their illness, or about the possibility that they will die.

The cancer patient is involved in the most remarkable, revelatory and learning experience of all of life. She is facing the possibility of death. For millenia mankind's best thinkers have reflected on this moment. Is death the end of life? Utter extinguishment of the human spirit? Blank nothingness? Or is there another mode of existence beyond death? Is there another dimension to life which will mean blinding glory? Fulfillment of all that life has meant? Will there be a deity to meet us on the other side? Will that personage greet us with kindly forgiveness? Or stern judgment? Will the transformed human find an Islamic god? A Judaic? A Christian? Or will the soul sink into the blissful nothingness of infinite being as is taught in Buddhism? Will the soul be reincarnated and become, say, a cockroach in the palace of a Middle Eastern sheik? An eagle soaring above the Rockies?

One would expect that the dying patient, or even a person in the early and perhaps curable stages of cancer, would be concerned about this and want to share her thoughts with loved ones or with clergy.

And the fact seems to be that many patients, though by no means all, *do want* to talk about death. But few engage in such discussions. The reason is not that they cannot bring themselves to do it, but that their parents, mates, children, friends, doctors, nurses, and even clergy shy away. It is odd that, unwittingly, those who love the cancer patient often refuse to do what he wants and needs most.

Even if the patient is not of a religious or philosophical mind, there are other matters to contemplate and resolve: financial arrangements, care of children, disposition of personal items and last words to loved ones.

One young woman who wanted to discuss her possible demise with her husband found it impossible.

You can't say to him, "Look, if I die . . . ." He'll say, "Hey! Don't die!" You'll never get your point across.

A man, years afterward, looks back at his wife's death:

She *tried* to talk about it. About dying. She wanted to talk about the children, how I should handle them. Even about my re-marriage! But I just couldn't handle it. I kept telling her she was going to make it. I wish now I had let her talk.

A young woman who later contracted cancer herself weeps as she remembers her father's death:

When my father died, they never used the word cancer. Ever, ever, ever. My mother knew, but she didn't tell us. You know? Why did they try to spare us? Why didn't they give us a chance to say to my father, "I love you a lot, Dad." I told him that two days before he died, but he was incoherent then and I'm not sure he even heard me.

Sometimes the refusal to discuss the disease and the possibility of death is particularly hard to understand. A Can-Surmount volunteer tells this story:

This lady was a real advocate of the Nazarene church. I figured she must have a Christian reference. But she and her husband never talked about his illness. It was just understood that they wouldn't discuss it. He ended up coming to the hospital for surgery. She'd be real grim-faced talking to me in the hall, but when he'd come she'd smile and say everything was fine. How can people be that full of emotions and deny them?

Occasionally, family members avoid discussions to protect the cancer patient. A leukemia patient describes this phenomenon:

We played games with each other. I was fine, even if I was so sick I couldn't hold up my head. He was the protector, was not going to let anything ever happen to me. He put me in a bubble. I was not allowed to talk about dying. I was not allowed to do anything where I might accidentally hurt myself. Or get tired. That went on until I couldn't handle it anymore. My son came home from school one day, and I had mowed the lawn. I hadn't been allowed to do that, even though I love it. Every time I did, I'd get yelled at by either my son or husband. Well, my son asked why I had mowed the lawn, said his father would be angry at me. I said, "Just leave me alone. I know what I can do and what I can't." Just then my husband walks in the door and jumps on me, and I really came unglued. For the first time my husband and son saw me scream and throw things. They were scared to death. I yelled at them: "You've got to let me do what I want to." They're still over-protective, but now they don't say anything.

Sometimes, perhaps most often, the subject is avoided because the family member himself cannot deal with it.

My husband's had a hard time facing it. Coming to see me was the first time he'd ever been in a hospital. So he walks in and almost passes out. I know he cares. If I didn't know that, I would probably have shot him a long time ago. But he can't face the emotional aspects. He doesn't know how. He has never been able to express emotions easily.

When I found out I had cancer the second time, I don't think he told anybody. He didn't want to hear about it. He took over, he'd clean house, he'd cook meals, he'd do anything that would take work off me. But for emotional support, he was the pits. One day I'd been having muscle spasms, what have you. I told him I was going in the next day for a brain scan, and he said, "Oh? Okay." He went out to the garage and started working on the car. That's his way of handling it. If I wanted to talk to him, I'd have to chase him around the house.

Patient after patient tells of yearning to discuss his cancer or his death. And the refusal of others to talk, probably intended to reassure the patient, actually contributes to the awful loneliness. The patient must lie in her bed, stare at approaching eternity, and contemplate the ultimate challenge of life by herself.

## FAMILY

Of course, many immediate families handle the shock well. And their support helps the cancer patient immeasurably. A Can-Surmount coordinator whose prognosis was particularly grim re-members with gratitude:

> My husband is a remarkable man. I can only attribute the fact of my coming to terms with it as soon as I did to his attitude. He is a total optimist. Pessimism is not in his vocabulary. He doesn't allow that kind of attitude. He is just a remarkable guy. I am sure he had a bad time handling it initially. He said what really saved his life is that he began jogging in earnest. He would run miles and miles and miles. He felt that was his salvation. When I was in the hospital in Edmonton he would get up so early the moon would still be up and go out jogging through the beautiful park that is near here. He has been more than supportive, more than sympathetic. He's a kind, warm, wonderful individual.

Another woman, who was considered to have hopeless colon cancer but recovered to become an enthusiastic CanSurmount vol-unteer, speaks with tenderness of her husband's love and help.

> From the beginning my husband and I have handled this together. In fact, one of our funny stories is that once George was talking about our cancer experience and someone asked, "Mr. Flexnor, where is your cancer?" He said, "In my wife's colon." Every time I went to the doctor, George went with me. Even after eleven years we still do that. Then we go out to lunch together to celebrate the good news.

A young artist who found he had testicular cancer looks back at his experience and says with admiration bordering on awe:

> My wife was my real strength. She is a really strong person. I don't know what I would have done without her, that's for sure. That's the one thing that really helped me the most. Her strength. And understanding.

A girl tells this touching story:

> My parents were very upset about my cancer. But they were real good. Not hysterical. They never showed much to me except that they were extremely concerned. But they never bawled or cried or got hysterical or anything like that. After the first operation I was in the recovery room and my mother and sister and dad came in to see me. I was in a real daze. I was so drugged and didn't know what was going on, only that I felt lousy. My sister, she must have been fifteen at the time, was wearing a sweater of mine. And the first thing I said when they walked in was, "Why are you wearing my sweater?" Poor Lisa felt so bad! She left the room immediately, and I knew later that it was to cry. My dad had a great comeback. It must have taken a lot of strength for him to say this. He said, "Oh, well, we really didn't know if you were going to make it out of the hospital so she's been wearing your clothes." [Laughs]. I was really glad he did that, sort of humbled me at the same time.

Young people in love have a particularly difficult challenge. It is amazing how many rise to the occasion with courage and dignity. One mother says that when her daughter discovered she was terminally ill of cancer, she told her fiancé immediately.

> She and her boyfriend were married—for fifteen months. He never left her side. She had a beautiful wedding. Three hundred people. But, well . . .

## FAILURE OF FAMILY

Human beings are rarely so mature as those described above. One woman who had cancer of the thyroid says with sadness:

> My husband told me quite frankly he was getting sick of hearing
> about it, you know? He thought, you get treated, you get well.

Having an engagement, even a marriage, collapse under the
weight of cancer is mercifully uncommon, but unfortunately it
does occur. One young woman who had already lost a kidney to
an infection, was living with her boyfriend when she discovered
she had breast cancer. Devastated, she returned to share the news
with the man she loved. He said, "Hey, that's heavy. I don't think
I can handle that." He moved out that night.

A retired military officer and former cancer patient who is a
CanSurmount volunteer tells a sad story.

> One young fellow has been in and out of the hospital for a couple
> of years. He's back in now, and he's in rough shape. His wife is
> divorcing him. While he's sick in the hospital here. God! I swear
> people are something!

With bitterness an able, charming CanSurmount coordinator
remembers her own experience:

> Three months into my chemo, my husband came to me—we'd
> had troubles in our marriage before I was diagnosed. He told me he
> really needed some time to get his head together, and since my
> folks lived not too far away, would I mind going there for awhile? I
> said, "Fine." He was my main support. I didn't want to lose him.
> I'd have done anything to make him feel more comfortable. I
> packed my bag, went to my folks. Ten days later I had a letter in
> the mail saying he had filed for divorce. I got incredibly depressed.
> I really didn't even know if I wanted to continue the chemo.

An older physician sighs and says,

> I have the neatest little gal you ever saw who has cancer of the
> breast. She told me yesterday she and her husband are separating.
> One of the reasons is they can't talk about her illness. She has gone
> through chemotherapy. The cancer has not returned, but . . . .

A CanSurmount coordinator in a Denver hospital says:

> A lot of wives come in here and say, "I can't take him home. I
> can't do it one more time."

One woman had a long fight against cancer, was cured and
later found she had another kind of cancer. She went home to her
husband, who had borne up well under the challenge of the first
occurrence, and told him the bad news. He became enraged,
shook a trembling finger at her and said, "Damn it! I can't take
that! I took it once, but no more!" During the long months of her
second surgery and chemotherapy, she never mentioned her illness
to him again.

The problem of mates being unable to accept or deal with
the reality of cancer is not restricted to laymen. One California
woman who has had a double mastectomy herself tells this story:

> I have a friend whose husband is a surgeon. Well, she went for a
> mammogram, and they found she had a tumor. Her husband was
> furious! He was horrid to her. I think he can't cope with it. So now
> she not only has to cope with the breast, but also with her
> husband. He's mad at her for going for the mammogram. They
> haven't done anything more yet, operated or anything!

Older children in the family are frequently angry that a parent has cancer because it disrupts their lives. An Oklahoma
woman says:

> The older kids, both of them, resented my being sick, because I
> couldn't do things for them I had done. So I felt guilty. Then
> they'd feel guilty for resenting it, and it turned into a vicious cycle.

A young woman who lost her mother when she was a teenager looks back today with horror at her attitude. During the
turbulent days of adolescence when she was becoming interested
in boys and competing with other girls for attention, her mother
was too sick to help. The daughter could never have a party in her
home, never bring friends home, never play loud music in her
own room. Finally, when her mother died, she admits she was
glad! The ordeal was over. But then for years she had to deal with
the guilt she felt. One can only speculate that her mother knew of
her resentment. That must have brought more loneliness.

Even *adult* offspring can fail to be supportive. A Denver

CanSurmount volunteer tells of a woman she visited for weeks before she died. The woman was divorced and had two daughters, one living in New York, one in Minnesota. She was always alone. Eventually, she received word that her New York daughter was coming to visit. She lived for that visit and died almost immediately afterward. The volunteer wrote a note to each of the daughters, telling about her death and about how much she had liked their mother. The volunteer says with angry sarcasm that both daughters replied that they thought it very kind of the volunteer to have visited their mother.

Another CanSurmount volunteer sighs:

Maybe the worst part is you know you get to be a bore to other people, especially your own family. Not only a burden but a bore! It's one thing to be sympathetic for three months, six months even. But year in and year out! Some of these families have gone on for years. People have no idea.

Another volunteer says that when she was undergoing radiation and chemotherapy her son wanted to drop out of college "to take care of you, Mom." He was not doing well and was looking for an excuse to quit. But more than anything in the world she wanted him to graduate.

It is not just children and mates who have trouble dealing with the reality of cancer. The wife of a young man who was found to have Stage IV Hodgkin's says they called his parents in New York to tell them the bad news.

They weren't really too supportive. We told his father, and his father said, "We won't tell your mother. . . ." Bill didn't lose his hair at all during his chemotherapy, so when his father came to visit, he said, "Gee, you couldn't have had it that bad. You didn't lose your hair." That hurt. He didn't know how bad it was. Then he went back to New York.

A Texas woman who had a long struggle with metastatic cancer says laconically:

All my mother ever wanted was for me to say, "I'm fine, mother. Everything is great." If I ever tried to say anything different, she'd change the subject. She couldn't handle it. She told me I'd never know how hard it was on her having a daughter with cancer.

## FRIENDS

A person with cancer does not stay at home and see only family members. He must also deal with neighbors and acquaintances, fellow workers, friends. And here again he is sometimes in for a surprising experience. Of course, some people are wonderful. One Canadian woman remembers the reaction of friends when she was diagnosed:

> I was fortunate. I have some marvelous friends. They weren't just sympathetic, they were *empathetic*. They were very helpful. Three in particular, very close women friends. They were marvelous. Initially, when I had just been told, before I went to the hospital, they didn't just . . . I think they had a schedule that was unwritten. I was never alone except when I wanted to be. They were tremendous.

But not all friends handle it so well. Most of us have never had to think about such things as life-threatening diseases. We do not know what to do or say. We sometimes try to avoid the issue by avoiding the person. And this leaves cancer patients hurt, confused and alone.

> The standoffishness of people! Believe me, when you come down with this disease, you find out who your friends are. I've seen instances with other patients, where so called bosom buddies, when they found out that person was a patient, just disappeared into the blue, had nothing more to do with the family.

A woman with a rare and particularly painful kind of bone cancer says:

> It is a hurtful thing when someone you had known, you see in a shopping center and they go the other way because they don't know what to say to you.

This "embarrassment" or "not knowing what to say" can lead to ridiculous actions.

I had friends who would come to the door, put a cake in my hands, start to cry and run out.

Another woman says stoically:

I don't discuss it with my friends. You've got it, so you might as well face it. But when I took my first radiation, well, all the people I worked with never asked me any questions. I wanted to talk about it. But I didn't want to force them to go through something they were uncomfortable with. So I didn't talk about it much. I don't even try now.

Of course, when one considers the kind of thing people say, it may be better if they *do* avoid a discussion. A common complaint among patients is illustrated by this quote:

I get statements from some of my friends, "You know, Herb, of all the people in the world that had to get it, *you* got it. You can handle it. You are a fighter." Well, God damn it, there are times when I get depressed!

Perhaps on occasion the unwillingness to deal with a friend's cancer is due to insensitivity or even stupidity. A young air force officer says:

Some of the dumb ones at work come up and ask, "How many more years do you have left to live? Got a couple more years?" I know they don't mean that in a mean way; it's their ignorance.

But it is usually more complicated than that. Some doctors have suggested that our reluctance springs from the fact that another person's cancer reminds us of our own mortality. We are forced to realize that we could have cancer ourselves someday, that we, too, will eventually die. A Colorado woman agrees. She thinks she is a walking reminder of things people want to forget. She tells this story:

My next door neighbor is a nice woman. One day she asked me if I wanted to come over to a Bible study at her home. I told her I couldn't come that day because I had chemotherapy scheduled. I never heard from her again except to say, "Hi," or something like that at the mail box. . . . I think people are afraid of getting attached. They don't want to get emotionally attached to someone with cancer. They might die on them. It scares them to be around somebody who might die.

A retired army officer says:

When people hear that some individual has cancer, they want to divorce themselves from that individual, get as far away as possible. It scares them. It's just the idea that the big "C" has carried the death verdict with it for so many years. "You have cancer? Forget it. You're gone."

Nor is this attitude confined to laymen who do not deal daily with disease and death. A nurse who was hospitalized for tests relates her experience.

Because I am a nurse I knew everyone in the hospital. Before surgery everybody was dropping in and having chocolates and visiting and kibitzing. But once the diagnosis got around, that indeed it was cancer, even though we didn't know how extensive, it was as if I had been diagnosed as having leprosy. People stayed away in droves. Suddenly nobody was stopping by to eat chocolates. I guess they lost their appetite. This made me feel as if things were worse than I had suspected. That was very difficult.

There are many other reasons people stay away. Despite decades of effort by the medical profession and the American Cancer Society to educate Americans about the nature of cancer, large numbers of people still believe cancer is contagious.

One guy at work asked me if I was still contagious, you know?

A CanSurmount volunteer tells a story which shows just how isolating this attitude can be:

I called on a woman who told me she was having troubles with her husband. He didn't understand the illness, didn't want to understand it. As we talked, he came into the room. So she introduced me, and he shook hands with me. She said to him, "This lady has had cancer too." He walked over to the sink and washed his hands. So, I excused myself. I said, "You go ahead and visit with your husband. I'll come back another time." I was down in the office and after—oh, I don't know how long he stayed— after he left I went back to see her and she was crying. I asked her about it, if it was always this way when he came. She said, "Well, usually. You know, we don't touch anymore. He thinks he's going to catch this from me. We have a little child, and he likes for me to be in the hospital because he thinks the baby will catch it from me, too."

Whatever the reason, friends and associates do tend to desert a cancer patient, causing loneliness which is almost unendurable. A CanSurmount volunteer says:

My friend had cancer for fifteen years and she said that nobody would talk to her. No one! Particularly as it progressed. There was just no one. It was the most horrible thing!

And another volunteer gives an extreme example:

I remember this one woman who had been bedridden for a long time. She lived alone. It was probably my most devastating experience, because I visited her regularly for a long time. And she slowly failed. I don't remember the kind of cancer. But what got me about her was that she was always alone. I never visited her when there was anyone else there. Except on one occasion. That was when I happened to be in her room and she had gone off for some procedure. So the room was empty, and someone came in who had known this woman and when she found the woman wasn't there—even though I told her she would be right back—her reaction was that she wanted to leave. She was very uncomfortable. Didn't really want to be there. I think it was some kind of duty call. She asked if there was something she could do for this woman. I told her she could stay and see her. But she didn't want to do that. That was the only time I ever saw anyone else there.

Perhaps the most balanced (and kind) summary of the way friends and acquaintances act was given by a woman who has fought cancer for more than fifteen years. She says with resignation:

Friends have got their lives and their problems to worry about. My friends were concerned, but they didn't want to hear about how many times I threw up, or my fear of dying. [Long pause] I have found friends to be basically supportive. But not in *talking* to me. They would not talk to me. Mostly they communicated through my husband.

## SUPPORT FROM RELIGION

One would expect that since families and friends so often fail to give support, cancer patients would turn to religion for solace. That seems to depend on how important religion was to them before the diagnosis. Those who were not religious rarely become so. Those who were, usually find their faith helpful. One devout Episcopalian woman who suffered from metastatic breast cancer said shortly before her death:

We are faithful members of St. Peter's, and we have gotten a tremendous amount of support from the church. Both from the clergy and from the people. Two churches are giving us support. We go to the weekly healing services at St. Paul's Church. It's very loving—the people there may not be able to handle the fact of my cancer totally, but they love us and support us.

A Presbyterian woman was approached by friends who wanted to bring a fundamentalist "healer" to pray over her. She politely declined and told her husband in private that she abhorred such "superstition" and wanted the "healer" kept away. She found great solace in reading her Bible and in prayer. She died in peace after confiding to her brother that she had no complaints.

A conservative Lutheran woman who survived harrowing experiences with bone cancer and metastases was scornful of the attempts of hospital chaplains to be comforting. She found their theology too "vague." But she spoke with enormous gratitude for the ministrations of her parish pastor.

A woman who lost her youngster to cancer says:

We're not Catholic, but Father Sullivan came over here Saturday, just before the second operation. A total stranger. He spent three hours with us. I was on the edge of breaking down. He saved me.

A Catholic woman critical of the lack of support she received from her own church (but who remains loyal to it) tells this story:

> I have a friend who is a born-again Christian. He was a drunk and rowdy electrician his whole life. But all of a sudden he had an experience, you know? He and his wife lived in Cedar Rapids, and my husband stayed with them while I was in the hospital. They came up to see me the night before surgery. They brought their minister, who is a really nice guy. He said, "Billy and Rachel have told me about your situation. I know you're probably afraid. Would you allow us to pray with you?" I said, "You betcha!" So all four of us sat there holding hands and praying. I felt wonderful. Just because he came. I didn't know him from Adam. He came one other time, then I never saw him again. But he took the time, and he knew that I was scared half out of my wits.

## CLERGY

It is disconcerting to discover how few cancer patients find clergy helpful. The most common criticism is expressed well by an outspoken young woman:

> If anything, the clergy are in a worse state than the doctors. I think they have a harder time dealing with death and dying. And when you're dealing with cancer in the advanced stages, where the person isn't going to make it, the person needs somebody who's extra-sensitive, to assure them that there is a hereafter. We're all going to die, and this is a predisposed thing that God has planned for us, and He will take care of us later. But they have a hard time conveying that.

A melanoma patient who is a faithful Catholic says with sorrow:

> Our first priest was a really holy person. He was loved by everyone. And he loved everyone. But he was uncomfortable talking about death. The new priest, he's such a private person that . . . . Well, we've never talked. Maybe someday I'll tie him in a chair and make him talk to me.

A common complaint is that the priest or minister is perfunctory running through religious rituals or prayers but as detached as the doctors can be. Another melanoma patient and Can-Surmount coordinator says:

> My parish priest came to the hospital and visited with my husband, in my room. And he came to the house and gave me communion and left. He never once asked me how I was feeling, how I was doing or anything. All of us in CanSurmount hear from people how the clergy let them down.

Another Catholic says:

> Father Mitchel, who is the chaplain at St. Mary's, ran in and heard my confession the night before my surgery. And he came in the morning and gave me communion. That was nice. But we didn't talk.

A young woman who had breast surgery recalls:

> I had surgery on Monday. Wednesday the preacher came to see me. When he walked in I started to cry. He wanted to know if something *else* had happened. Ha! The poor man didn't know how to handle it.

Sometimes the complaint is that the clergyman gives such inappropriate advice or intellectually vapid comfort that they are more infuriating than helpful. A young man who was confined in a military hospital for his treatment remembers:

> There was this one Baptist minister, a chaplain, who kept coming around. He pressed himself on us. We were polite. But he talked about, "It's God's will," "God's doing something special with you." That kind of crap. I was polite. But it got to the point where we would sit in the room and not say anything. He'd bring up things and I'd say, "That's good." We'd stare at each other for five minutes.

Sometimes the clergyman is more interested in programs he is pushing in his church than he is in the feelings of a cancer patient. A CanSurmount volunteer says:

My pastor . . . we have these cell groups where we have meetings in homes. Instead of my having a group meeting in my home, I spend my time in the hospital. My pastor is always talking to me about, "You ought to get involved in the Agape thing. We really need your house for this meeting." But I say to him that I'm needed more at the hospital than I am there.

By far the most common complaint about the clergy is the same as the one about doctors. They don't seem to care. They are not personal. And that complaint is repeated about every denomination or faith. A kindly, devout Catholic who lost his wife says:

I don't think Helen ever took her problem to the priest. How could he help you? I think *people* can help you, but ministers can't. It shouldn't be . . . well, a person knowing he is dying, and he'd much rather be up front about it. Help get his unfinished business finished, make peace.

What could a priest or minister, the average one, do to help you when you can go to a friend who will put her arms around you, nurture you and care for you? That is a lot more beneficial than going either to a priest or minister. Have them get a book out and read a prayer about it. They can deal with *birth*, you know? That's great. A joyous occasion. They can baptize into the community of the church. That's great. But when it comes to dying . . . . There are probably some who can sit down with somebody, take somebody's hand and talk about it. But I don't think there are many. Nobody did it with us. Oh, they came and asked, "How are you doing?" Things like that. I think priests, ministers, they should be friends, too. Cancer is lonely!

Lynn Ringer tells these two revealing stories:

It was after the first surgery. I was still real sick. A young man, nice looking fellow in a suit and tie, came into my room. He didn't have a collar, and I had no idea who he was until I noticed his name tag. He was a hospital chaplain. He was really formal, stood at the end of the bed. He began by commenting about all my cards and flowers, and chit-chatted for a few minutes. He never asked if I wanted to pray or anything, though I assumed that was his role. His whole presence was one of being real nervous and uncomfortable. I could have cared less that he was there, but I worked hard to make him feel more at ease.

A young intern, about my age, who was part of the 'team' of doctors ministering to me, came in one day. He had on a white jacket. I was lying on my side with the rails of the bed up. The naso-gastric tube was in, and I was feeling really low. This intern came over to the bed, pushed aside all the bottles and stuff on the bedside table, knelt down, put his forearms on the table and laid his head on his arms and looked through the bars at me. "I am so sorry," he said. That was all. And it made all the difference. He was a friend.

If the above experiences are typical, it should not surprise us that some patients become atheists. One lovely woman who worked with CanSurmount for years and gave comfort and friendship to many patients explains her attitude:

I always considered myself religious although I was not a church-goer. I grew up being sent to Sunday School. My parents never went themselves, but they sent me to church. I won all the stars and medals and those things. I had the feeling that I lived a sort of charmed life, that God took care of me. Then this happened and I looked to religion for help. But I found I couldn't get help that way. So, instead of finding solace in religion, I found it in rejecting religion. I realized I was not religious or agnostic but plain out and out atheist. So I never had any communication with a clergyman at all.

Thus, the loneliness for at least that one cancer patient was extended to the ultimate. Not only did she perceive her doctors as uninterested in her except as a case, her friends withdrawing, her family bored, her clergy unwilling to talk, she also concluded that the universe had no interest in her.

# 7
# Almost Like VD

In spite of all that has been said, the loneliness of the cancer patient is difficult to explain in full. An elderly lady says,

I hate cancer. People think it is something like . . . contagious. Almost like VD, and you have to be ashamed to talk about it.

A man remembers:

The isolation of cancer is bad. If they just wouldn't treat you like a leper! A non-person, abandoned by everyone.

And a young military officer says bitterly:

There are a lot of us out there living normal lives. We're not the dregs of society. We're not Typhoid Marys.

Victims of a heart attack are not so shunned. As one cancer victim said, "Huh! If you've had a heart attack, it's like a badge. It means you've been a hard worker, a go-getter." And those who have had a stroke or are stricken with kidney disease or a host of other life-threatening diseases are not so ostracized. There is even something romantic about tuberculosis. To some extent myths persist that "TB" is the disease of extremely intelligent persons who are too sensitive and passionate to live successfully in this harsh world.

But there is a stigma attached to cancer, "a belief that it is dirty or unclean or catchy," as one patient described it. This wide-

spread revulsion comes from more than the ignorant fear of con-
tagion. Certainly, the vast majority of Americans today know it is
not contagious. Cancer *is* frightening, but should it be more so
than other potentially, or even positively, fatal diseases?

Cancer patients also maintain that others see the disease as a
shameful thing. And among the ignorant and superstitious the
once common explanation that cancer is caused by "sin" persists.
One lady who went to a religiously supported nursing home to die
reported that a caller from the parent church said, "You know, if
you really believed in Jesus Christ as your personal saviour, you
would never have gotten sick. And you'd be healed instantly if you
confessed your faith now." A charming, elderly (deeply religious)
lady who had been sick with a variety of ailments before finally
succumbing to cancer smiled at such statements.

> Some people with cancer think, "Maybe I've sinned somewhere in
> my life." But I look back on *my* life, and I don't think I'm too
> different from others. We see sinners who are very sinful, and they
> go their merry way and have no problems. I will be sixty-seven
> years old in another month. I've been a lot of places and seen a lot
> of people. Some of the ones we've been very close to, who've been
> the best Christians you could hope for, they've been the ones
> who've been hurt the most.

The thought that people somehow cause their own disease,
or deserve it, appears in different forms. The modern version of
the "Sin Causation" theory is that if one takes care of himself,
stays away from junk food, jogs tens of miles each week, eschews
smoking and excessive drinking, represses no emotions and eats a
pound of vitamins daily, he will escape the scourge of cancer. A
melanoma victim said,

> I couldn't figure it out. I never smoked, hardly ever drank, took
> good care of myself. I thought I was a pretty decent person. Why
> did this happen to me? It shouldn't happen to me. I know people
> who're doing dope and beating their kids and nothing ever happens
> to them. Why me?

Who among us has not had a friend hospitalized for cancer
and heard someone comment, "Well, you know, he didn't take
care of himself. You never saw him on the tennis court, and he

was fifteen pounds overweight." The inference is that he was pun-
ished for the "sin" of not "taking care of himself." Perhaps the
persistence of this kind of thinking explains the stigma.

But there is another myth current in our culture: the belief
that cancer is an expression, or the result, of a type of personality.
There has been a great deal of discussion about the "cancer personality." Susan Sontag, in a brilliant little book, *Illness As Meta-
phor*, lists many examples:

> A study by Dr. Caroline Bedell Thomas of the Johns Hopkins
> University School of Medicine was thus summarized in one recent
> newspaper article ("Can Your Personality Kill You?"): "In brief,
> cancer victims are low-gear persons, seldom prey to outbursts of
> emotion. They have feelings of isolation from their parents dating
> back to childhood." Drs. Claus and Marjorie Bahnson at the
> Eastern Pennsylvania Psychiatric Institute have "charted a
> personality pattern of denial of hostility, depression and of memory
> of emotional deprivation in childhood" and "difficulty in
> maintaining close relationships." Dr. O. Carl Simonton, a
> radiologist in Fort Worth, Texas, who gives patients both radiation
> and psychotherapy, describes the cancer personality as someone
> with "a great tendency for self pity and a markedly impaired ability
> to make and maintain meaningful relationships." Lawrence
> LeShan, a New York psychologist and psychotherapist (You Can
> Fight for Your Life: Emotional Factors in the Causation of Cancer
> [1977]), claims that "there is a general type of personality
> configuration among the majority of cancer patients" and a
> worldview that cancer patients share and "which predates the
> development of cancer." He divides "the basic emotional pattern of
> the cancer patient" into three parts: "a childhood or adolescence
> marked by feelings of isolation," the loss of the "meaningful
> relationship" found in adulthood, and a subsequent "conviction
> that life holds no more hope." "The cancer patient," LeShan
> writes, "almost invariably is contemptuous of himself, and of his
> abilities and possibilities." Cancer patients are "empty of feelings
> and devoid of self."

Blaming the patient for having a disease the physician can't
accurately diagnose or adequately treat is a venerable practice in
medicine. It's easy to assume that the patient is unhappy in marriage or at work. But while many researchers would admit that

emotional trauma or other illness may depress immunity and permit a latent tumor to appear, few would want to suggest that cancer is *caused* by wrong thinking or by inappropriate dealing with stress. Anyone who has known numerous cancer patients, particularly before their disease appeared, would surely doubt the cancer personality theory. Are we to think that John Wayne and Humphrey Bogart had "a great tendency for self pity"? That John Foster Dulles was a "low-gear person"? That Napoleon, Ulysses S. Grant, Robert A. Taft, and Hubert Humphrey were "contemptuous of themselves" and "devoid of feelings"?

The ultimate result of such proposals is that the patient is blamed for his own illness. A particularly thoughtful CanSurmount coordinator says angrily:

> I think people have enough problems without getting accused of being responsible for their own cancer. How do you reconcile that to people? That's why I don't like [the Simontons]. It places too much guilt on people who have a lot of problems to deal with already.

Susan Sontag put it even more forcefully.

> In Karl Menninger's more recent formulation: "Illness is in part what the world has done to a victim, but in larger part it is what the victim has done with his world and with himself . . ." Such preposterous and dangerous views manage to put the onus of the disease on the patient and not only weaken the patient's ability to understand the range of plausible medical treatment but also, implicitly, direct the patient away from such treatment. Cure is thought to depend principally on the patient's already sorely tested or enfeebled capacity for self-love.

Later, she says,

> Psychological theories of illness are a powerful means of placing the blame on the ill. Patients who are instructed that they have, unwittingly, caused their disease are also being made to feel that they deserved it.

She points out that modern proponents of the ancient theory claim repression of emotions is the "sin."

As once TB was thought to come from too much passion, afflicting
the reckless and sensual, today many people believe their cancer is
a disease of insufficient passion, afflicting those who are sexually
repressed, inhibited, unspontaneous, incapable of expressing anger.

And to this "Me Generation" which believes the worst of all
sins is to deny oneself anything, including expression of whatever
stray hostile thoughts are meandering through the mind, repression is a shocking and shameful thing. Of course, it was not always
so. In previous generations the advice was different.

As a prophylaxis against cancer, one [nineteenth century] English
doctor urged his patients "to avoid over-taxing their strength, and to
bear the ills of life with equanimity; above all things, not to 'give
way' to any grief." Such stoic counsels have now been replaced by
prescriptions for self-expression, from talking it out to the primal
scream. (Sontag, ibid.)

A frustrating part of the cancer personality theory is that it
seems impossible ever to prove it wrong. If one points out that
Hubert Humphrey was anything but self-hating, a proponent of
the theory can reply that deep down, beneath the surface of his
bubbling personality Humphrey despised himself because he had
been unsuccessful in securing the presidency. If one questions that
John Wayne was devoid of self, the psychologist can answer that
beneath the confidence lurked a feeling that his he-man bravado
was silly. If a critic recalls that Freud died of cancer of the jaw, the
psychologist says that shows how insecure he was in his theories
and pronouncements. If one observes that CanSurmount volunteers are unusually vivacious and courageous people, he smiles
smugly and notes that they are the survivors. They have risen
above their originally contemptible personalities and become more
like, say, the psychologist. There is not way to disprove the cancer
personality theory except to find the real cause of cancer.

Perhaps the attempt to explain the "reason" one person is
stricken so cruelly and another enjoys a life of superb health pro-
ceeds from feelings of guilt within the healthy person. During the
evil days of segregation and the denial of human rights to black
people, there was always an attempt to justify the "system" by saying that the victims deserved their unjust treatment. Blacks were
said to be lazy, dirty and stupid. Maybe the stigma attached to

cancer is an unconscious attempt by the healthy person to justify his good fortune and his desire to avoid the unpleasantness of associating with the less fortunate. Perhaps the practice among physicians of blaming patients for falling victim to a disease they cannot cure comes from the same guilt. Sontag says,

> Theories that diseases are caused by mental states and can be cured by will power are always an index of how much is not understood about the physical terrain of a disease.

Anyone who has met hundreds of cancer patients will admit that they include every imaginable kind of person. It seems clear that cancer falls upon "the just and the unjust, the righteous and the unrighteous." Certainly, anyone who knows Carvel and Ernestine McWilliams will laugh at the suggestion that cancer afflicts those who despise themselves or repress their emotions. Both were afflicted with cancer. Ernestine had a painful skin cancer and Carvel a cancer of the lymph system. Far from being a timid person unable to express himself, Carvel is a retired salesman who will make a speech at the drop of a hat. Ernestine is a cheerful, pretty woman who commutes weekly to Presbyterian Medical Center to call on new cancer patients. They epitomize what is the most powerful argument against the cancer personality theory. Most young, healthy people cannot bring themselves to associate with cancer patients. It is depressing and reminds them of the possibility they, too, may some day fall victim to the disease. But the McWilliamses, both now in their seventies, have a far more healthy attitude toward cancer.

The same can be said of the indomitable Viola "Sid" Kline, who was stricken early in life with breast cancer. By the time it was discovered it had already spread to the lymph nodes. The surgeon gave her six months to live. Twenty four years later she went (with six other women from across the United States) to the White House to receive from Nancy Reagan a crystal eagle for being a Distinguished Volunteer of the Year. In her astonishing years of struggle against the disease which eventually killed her, Sid had worked unceasingly at first one and then another cause. For she spent those precious years while death waited impatiently in the wings in helping others, not indulging herself in self-pity or seeking pleasure. Near the end she said, "I couldn't spend my life doing nothing. Oh, I used to do ceramics and painting, and I love antiques. But that was just for *me*. I wanted to do something that would make my life worth something."

Far from fleeing "stress," she courted it. She served as a counselor at a mental health center, often dealing with violent people. She nudged the Woman's Club into supporting a program for battered women, and she visited endlessly for CanSurmount. But *her* visits were different. For in her later years she decided to become a clown. She went to school, learned her art, and used it to encourage and entertain cancer patients. But the most amazing thing about Sid was the way she handled her own treatment. She never let her doctors control her life. She would take radiation or chemotherapy for a time, then decide she needed a "furlough" from it and go her merry way, working, helping others, laughing, exulting in life.

Cancer is almost certainly due to an organism or substance which disturbs the DNA of the cell. Surely it is not the "fault" of the victim. Yet it is alarming how fast that notion is still growing. Even some physicians give credence to it. Andrew Weill, who trained at Harvard Medical School and who has written *The Natural Mind*, a book widely admired by younger doctors, has said:

> My experiences in allopathic medicine, both as a patient and as a
> practitioner, have led me to conclude that all illness is
> psychosomatic. . . . I mean that all illness has both psychic and
> physical components, and it seems to me that the physical
> manifestations of illness (including the appearance of germs in
> tissues) are always effects, while the causes always lie within the
> realm of the mind, albeit the unconscious mind. In other words,
> the disease process seems to me to be initiated always by changes in
> consciousness.

One cannot but wonder if Dr. Weill would then reject treatment if he were bitten by a rabid dog, preferring, perhaps, meditation to soothe his troubled spirit. And one may find it difficult to resist a trace of satisfaction from the following told by a faithful young Catholic woman who went to her priest to talk about her cancer:

> This priest was a really vivacious person who skied every day and
> played tennis. He was Polish, and he had a thick accent. He said,
> "I exercise effery day. I take goot care uff myself. I am very

healthy." We talked about my cancer, and he said, "Ach! You take good care of yourself, you exercise, you eat right, you lead a long, healthy life." Okay, he was only fifty-five. Two weeks later he died of a cerebral hemmorhage.

Whether the causes of the cancer patient's loneliness be pain and the fear of death, concern for her family, the refusal of others to talk, or the stigma attached to cancer, the loneliness remains. And occasionally that loneliness causes strange behavior. Betty Rollin, in her book, *First You Cry*, tells of going through a complete life change. She left her husband and ran off with another man. Then she left that man and drifted.

Another young woman described what happened when she became a cancer patient.

> I got crazy for awhile. You are faced with a problem of "Who am I?" "What's going to make me happy?" And many of us don't know that. We go in all sorts of directions, until the dust settles and we know just who we are. You're never more naked than when you've had a diagnosis of cancer.

# 8
# The Family

It is easy to blame others, especially family members, for the way cancer victims are treated. But it is also important to remember the tremendous strains families must endure. Most have never before had the experience of dealing with serious illness. Few have been so prudent or successful as to have adequate financial resources. When a loved one develops a malignancy the horror that descends is hard to imagine. Family members are quickly overwhelmed. To quote Bobby Colby, who succeeded Lynn Ringer as CanSurmount coordinator of Colorado, "Cancer is a weird disease. When one person gets it, the whole family gets it." A young man who survived a long battle with cancer says of his wife,

> We've both had cancer. You know what I mean? I have the
> physical end of it, but she feels the pain as much or sometimes
> more. I'm always tended to, but she's the family member who's
> accepted because she's there, but sometimes ignored.

A family with each person working toward his own dreams and goals must suddenly center its attention on the sick one. And many times family members do not even know how to treat the patient. Should they coddle her or be 'tough'? Should they discuss the disease or avoid the subject?

Cancer patients can be difficult to live with. They are scared, often in pain, miserable from chemotherapy, resentful at having the disease. Some times they take out their anger on family members. The mother of a boy who died says:

His personality changed. Sometimes I think the medication is what did it. David would get very, very mean. Literally mean! Then he'd come back and say, "I'm sorry." He knew it, but he couldn't control it.

The stresses can be horrendous. A Colorado woman who lost her husband remembers:

I and my four kids, why . . . it just tears a family apart! The amount of time you spend in the hospital, just sitting there! It gives you . . . you get tired. Jim ended up in the hospital for three months, which is a long time. The hospital is strange. You're worried. It's inconvenient. The expense worries you. Your routine is disrupted. You don't know how it's going to come out. And people, even hospital people who were very good to us, they didn't know what we were going through.

Few of us are natural heroes. We are weak human beings who have rarely been tested. And cancer never asks if we are ready for the challenge. On top of emotional pressures, it requires that we carry a bed pan, give shots, bathe a wound, change bandages, constantly attend the sick one. It sentences us to listen to complaints and sometimes cries of pain, to watch suffering and be helpless to alleviate it. It frequently reduces one we love to an emaciated, weak shadow. The mind recoils from such horror. A woman suffering from metastatic cancer says:

My husband has a hard time. He can't show emotion. He car-pooled with this guy for over a year and a half after I was diagnosed. The guy didn't know I had cancer. I was over half way through my chemotherapy, and his wife called me. She said, "Louise, why didn't you tell me you had cancer?" I said, "I thought everybody down there knew it." She said my husband had mentioned it to Jim in an off-hand way, like: "Everything will get back to normal at our house as soon as Louise gets through with her chemotherapy." Like a bombshell. He hadn't told anyone. I don't know how he could do that. It wasn't just that he didn't want to hear what I had to say, he wasn't talking about it himself.

Sometimes the problems are complicated by other factors. Lynn Ringer remembers one of her most painful experiences:

The lady had pancreatic cancer, and that's pretty miserable. She was a tiny lady, tougher than nails. But really nice. Her husband was an alcoholic. This got to be more and more annoying as she became really ill. I remember going to see her at home. I tried to visit with her husband in the kitchen and with her on the couch. He was falling apart. And that precipitated more drinking. I felt so sorry for him, a really nice man. You could see her getting more and more brittle about their relationship. Because he wasn't *available*. She needed him. It wasn't that he didn't *want* to help. He just couldn't do it.

When she was back in the hospital, the morning she died, I was in her room, and he was out in the waiting room. It was tough for him, even to be in her room, she looked so awful. So emaciated. She didn't look like herself at all.

She didn't know who I was. But she said, "I've got to get over to the other side!" I'll never forget that. I have no idea, of course, what she was talking about. She said it about three times, and I was boggled by it.

I walked out of the room and she died a few minutes after that. A nurse was with her. We got her husband. He was stunned by the whole thing. I wanted something romantic, you know. I hoped he would go in there and . . . . Well, he couldn't do that. That was such a sad family situation.

And family members are lonely, too. Recall the man whose wife walked the lonesome valley. Members of families struggling with cancer talk of *their* isolation. Mates either have to trudge to and from the hospital, or be tied to the home, unable to go out. They feel the world is passing them by. Friends and other family members are concerned about the sick one, but rarely worry about the spouse. And, understandably, this often causes resentment. A woman says sympathetically:

One of my husband's biggest complaints when I was first diagnosed was that everybody, *everybody*, would ask, "How's Karen doing?" They never asked how *he* was doing.

A woman who survived a malignant lymphoma says,

I always put in a plug for spouses of cancer patients. I think they really deserve some loving care. They go through more, at least as much. They don't have any control over it. Nor does the cancer patient, of course. But you *know your own body*, how you *feel*. So, at least in my own case, I think it was worse on my husband than it was on me. I have thought so many times I would not want to change places with him. The patient gets all the "glory," the husband all the suffering.

Mates often feel they must be cheerful, even when they are devastated and terrified. A middle-aged woman whose husband died after a long battle with prostatic cancer says, "If I had walked in that room and Bill had found me upset, it would have upset him further." A husband said, in the presence of his terminally ill wife:

It's a very difficult situation. Most people don't know anything about it when they start. Then you talk to a lot of people and learn as much as you can. You just try to be supportive. And . . . I happen to be a total optimist. Which helps. [Pause] I think.

His wife smiled gratefully and asked,

Have you heard the story about the thousand pound stone? A girl went away to college. After about two weeks her mother gets a telephone call. The girl says she feels as if she has a thousand pound stone on her shoulders. She's flunked two of her first tests, her roommate is awful and she hates college. Well, the mother worried for days. Finally, her husband says, "Why don't you call Suzy?" So she does, and Suzy is at a party having a wonderful time. The mother finally gets through to her the next day, and Suzy says, "Oh, I'm not worried anymore. I gave *you* my thousand pound stone."

Well, I put my thousand pound stone on him. [Points at husband] He seems to take it willingly. I don't know if that is good, but he takes it.

Every mate of a cancer patient has at least a part of the thousand pound stone, whether he wants it or not.

One of the problems families face is knowing when to talk with the patient about serious matters. Is it better to keep up a facade of complete optimism? Or does that make it more difficult for the patient to talk about the progress of the disease or his approaching death? A middle-aged man who lost his wife looks back:

> You go along, hoping that something will happen and put things in a state of remission and give you a few more years. And by doing that you don't face the truth. Maybe that is a good way of doing it, I don't know. You've *got* to have hope. I was never as good as I should have been, could have been, as far as being sensitive to and sharing Dorothy's thoughts and talking about a lot of things. I have learned a lot since. I realize now I could have helped her. I realized it right after she died. You always assume a certain amount of guilt.

The healthy mate is usually the one who must face the financial problems caused by cancer. Though today most Americans have some form of health insurance, there are a thousand expenses that are not covered. For example, the husband may resort to prepared food, or to taking the family out for meals, he may bring his wife books or flowers several times a week. He may buy another television set with a remote control she can handle from her bed. He may take the grieving children to movies or other entertainment to help them cope. That can mean getting someone to stay with the younger children or with his wife. He may have to hire someone to care for her while he works or takes necessary business trips. Such expenses are rarely covered by insurance. Furthermore, it is exceedingly difficult to find a good housekeeper. Many are grouchy, complain constantly about how much trouble the cancer patient is. They do sloppy work, or treat the children harshly. It is a fortunate family who can find good help at such a time.

When it is the husband who is stricken, the wife is confronted with equal and sometimes heavier burdens. The family's income can be reduced suddenly and remain low while the husband recuperates. Or, if the illness is terminal, he may be pensioned by his company. Income is further diminished. Since many older women have spent their lives as homemakers, the widow may not be accustomed to handling business affairs. She may have no marketable skills, in which case she will be forced to take a low paying job with few benefits. She may have to give up her home.

A distraught New Jersey woman whose husband died of a brain tumor decided she could no longer bear to remain in their home. She sold it, at a poor price, then could find no other house she liked. She tried to buy hers back, but the new owners, under-standably, refused. Another woman moved to be near her grown children and found she did not have enough money to live in the more expensive area. A lady from New Hampshire found herself widowed in her early forties with six children to support. Her hus-band had been a successful inventor, but the firm he had founded shortly before his death was tottering on the brink of bankruptcy. She managed to turn it into a successful enterprise. But that re-quired so much time her children resented her lack of attention. Soon after the last child reached adulthood, she, too, developed cancer and died.

And for the mate of a cancer patient there is always the prob-lem of sheer exhaustion. Endless hours are spent at the hospital, or caring for the patient at home, while trying to work. If there are children, they are terrified of losing a mother or father and the mate must constantly reassure them, keep them on as normal a schedule as possible, take them to school affairs alone. All this leaves the mate worn out. Yet many have trouble sleeping, some-times because the patient needs assistance during the night, more often because of worry and sorrow.

Time pressures can become impossible. Some mates are not free to take off from work to be with their sick or dying loved one. Many employers do not want to be bothered with an employee who is late to or absent from work. And the employee does not dare let the quality of his work fall or he may be fired.

Nor does cancer in a family cause life's day-to-day problems to vanish, or preclude the occurrence of other crises. They re-main, causing vast complications and more pressures. One woman remembers:

> Right in the middle of the time Elton had cancer, my father (he was seventy-eight then) developed a little lump right in front of his ear. He'd been living out here since my mother died eight years before. Finally, I said, "Dad, you've got to go and have that looked at." He went to a doctor, who sent him to a surgeon. It was malignant.

A woman from a farming area of Colorado was grief stricken when her husband developed a serious cancer of the lymph nodes. Then just as he began to show improvement, her son developed cancer of the testicles. The husband lived, the son died. A man whose wife was near death from metastatic breast cancer got a call from his sister that her husband had been killed in an automobile accident. The sorrowing sister moved her family to be close to her brother. A man who had extensive surgery for stomach cancer says:

> That was pretty hard on my wife. Then, after I recovered, we decided to move to Colorado, retire there. But with packing, and the strain she'd had when I was in the hospital, it all added up. She told me she had begun to have chest pains while I was in the hospital. But she didn't pay any attention to them. So, the twenty-fifth of October, she awakened me and said, "You'd better get me to the hospital." I took her to emergency, and called her internist. He was there very quickly. She was admitted to coronary care immediately. So she spent *her* time in the hospital, then we had to delay departure a month while she recuperated. Meanwhile, our furniture was already loaded and on its way out here. . . .

A CanSurmount volunteer remembers another example:

> The lady had other family problems in addition to her own cancer. Her husband turned out to have diabetes. Just this morning she told me her son, who is twenty-five and lives in California, has melanoma. Lydia had her mastectomy five years ago, then because the tests were positive, she had a hysterectomy. She's had a rough time. They just discovered this tumor on her son, a very large one on his abdomen. She said they cut out a huge piece. They're going to send him to a specialist. So I don't know. . . . But that melanoma, it's a devil of a disease.

The mate of the cancer patient may find that she has to fight even to get the care her husband needs. One CanSurmount volunteer says with admiration:

> My wife took care of everything. She is much stronger than I am to the extent that when I complained about the nurses, she'd go and fight them. She didn't get anywhere, but she fought! She was very supportive. She worked, and didn't miss any work. She called every noon that I was home.

A woman says, "If Kim took an abnormal breath, I called the doctor. I went through hell, too." A man in New York found that his wife, who had endured a radical mastectomy less than forty-eight hours before, had not received her pain shot. The nurses insisted she *had* been given the shot. The wife and another patient in the room were certain she had not. The man begged, pleaded and finally threatened until his wife, who was writhing in pain, was given the shot.

And the family must sometimes decide when to stop fighting. Every surviving mate can tell a story like this one:

> That night I sat beside her and watched her chest heave as she tried
> to breathe. My God! She was so thin I could see the ribs through
> her nightgown. I prayed that she would die. She had suffered
> enough. She died the next morning, and I was glad.

It is less common now than in years past, but even today some doctors will tell a patient virtually nothing. They confide only in the mate. The mate must then decide whether or how to tell the other that the CAT scan was a disaster, that tests showed the leukemia had resumed its progress, or that the pain in the leg is caused by a recurrence.

There are a hundred other torments unimagined by those who have never gone through the experience. A woman from the midwest tells of how she watched her husband slowly lose his fight against brain cancer. Again and again he was hospitalized. He became weaker and weaker, was finally bedridden for weeks. She found that she was looking at every man she met at the market, the church or the office as a potential new husband and father for her children. Then she felt guilty, berating herself for considering other men while her husband was going through hell.

A young woman found that she had cancer of the breast. When tests showed it had already metastasized to the bones, a oophorectomy was performed. She survived the cancer, but was heartbroken that she could not have children. She and her husband felt they could not adopt a child for fear the cancer would return and the foster child would be faced with the loss of his mother. It was difficult for the woman. But her husband was equally dismayed. He had eagerly looked forward to being a father.

Cancer in the family can be terrible for the children. Young ones rarely understand the gravity of the situation, but they can become frightened by talk they hear in the home. One wise young woman relates this incident:

My children were both so little I don't think either of them realized what was going on. The oldest one, on the way home from the doctor's said, "Mommy, if they take your eye out, how can you read me a story?" I said, "I'll still have my other eye." He said, "Okay," and went back to looking at his book.

A young woman in New York was dying of Hodgkin's. She was the stepmother of three children who had already lost a mother to suicide. The stepmother was unusually courageous and loving, and she did all she could to cushion the shock. But there was a minimal amount she could do. One day the seven year old girl came to her with a picture she had drawn of a young woman lying in a coffin. The child said simply, "This is the way you will look at your funeral." The woman said she ached more for the child than she did for herself.

A woman dying of metastatic breast cancer had severe bowel obstruction. As a result, she was constantly shaken with projectile vomiting which she could not control. Her children were appalled. Frequently, to the critically ill mother's own grief, they had to help clean up the mess.

Some cancer patients are ingenious about helping their children deal with the horror. A young Arizona woman had an eye removed. Her children were frightened of the black patch she had to wear until she got her prosthesis. One of her young sons had a birthday within a few days of her return from the hospital. Concerned that his friends would also be frightened, she gave the birthday party a pirate theme and invited each child to come dressed appropriately!

Children must often shoulder additional responsibilities or make sacrifices not asked of them before. Sometimes they must take over the cooking, do more housework, or assume duties with a garden or lawn. One brilliant young man who had high grades all his life, and who eventually became a National Merit Scholar, saw his grades drop precipitously when his mother's cancer recurred. Frequently college must be delayed because of the additional expenses.

The worst nightmare for any child is losing a mother or father. When cancer appears that nightmare intensifies or becomes a reality. And in addition, the child begins to wonder if she herself will develop the same cancer. This is particularly true of daughters of women with breast cancer. One mother who recovered from the primary breast tumor and from metastases to the bones says her daughter "became paranoid." The teenager had recurring night terrors that she was losing her breasts to the disease.

And as adults often treat cancer patients and their families insensitively, so it is with children. One young man recalls with pain his mother's long struggle with cancer. As her condition worsened, adult neighbors began to discuss it openly, and their children actually taunted him that his mother was dying. Mercifully, that is an uncommon experience. But it is lamentably common for the offspring of cancer patients to be shunned by other children. Sometimes the parents of these children, believing the disease to be contagious, are to blame. Or they may not want their youngsters associating with one who will remind them of the possibility of death. At the very least the child whose parent has cancer is hardly "fun" company. So loneliness is not confined to mates or to the patient herself. It can also be destructive of children.

When it is a child who falls ill with cancer, the parents are devastated. One family, unable to deal with the daughter's terminal illness, virtually shunned her. That is an extreme example, but it is not rare. Fortunately, and as we would expect, most parents fight to the utmost to save a son or daughter, however difficult it is. One woman who lost her son says,

> Each day we said, and I made him say it every day, *made him say it:* "I'm going to get well." We talked about it, we planned, we did things.

But it is hard for most parents to know just how to deal with the child who has cancer. Some spoil him, some act as if nothing has happened and refuse to discuss the issue. Few parents have experience to guide them. A young woman who lost a leg to cancer advises:

> I remember, up with the handicapped skiers, there was a boy, who had lost an arm, and he wanted me to hand him his pole. I was standing there on one leg, holding onto my outriggers. I said, "You've got two legs, get it yourself!" He did. He had been babied too much at home. *My* folks said, "If you need help, ask for it. Don't be upset if we don't do it without your asking. We don't want to do more than you want us to do." It is irritating when people,

out of kindness or pity or what, do more for you than you want done.

To see a child, or even an adult offspring, suffer, endure chemotherapy, radiation or perhaps extensive surgery, and be unable to help is one of the worst tortures possible for a parent. A Colorado mother recalls:

It just about killed us both. We worked as a team. We lived for Beth. I nursed her when she was at home, and whenever she was at the hospital—which was constantly. It was just in and out, in and out. The nurses taught me everything. I even gave her shots and changed her subclavian. I moved into the hospital every time she went in. I slept there. Never left her side. My husband and I would take shifts. Four years of hell. That's what it was!

We like to think of our old age as golden years of contentment and peace, a time when we accept the rewards of a life of service and responsibility, when we enjoy our grandchildren and delight in how well our children have grown to adulthood. But if an adult offspring succumbs to cancer it can be a terrible time. One man remembers the ordeal of his wife's parents.

Her mother and father were there, each in their seventies. They had done everything they could. She had come and nursed her daughter whenever possible. He helped with the expenses. That day they stood and watched her struggling to breathe. I said something—I don't remember what—and as I spoke, I could feel something wrong in the room. Then I knew—it was the oxygen. It was hissing because she wasn't breathing anymore. I said, "She's gone." Her father looked like death himself. But he said, "Good! Now she won't suffer anymore." Her mother started to cry, then said, really agitated, "Why couldn't it have been *me*? I've *had* my life!" He put his arm around her.

Grief and all its manifestations affect every member of the family. A man whose wife fought a long battle with metastatic breast cancer remembers:

The three little ones came into Faith's room to kiss her before they left for school. She couldn't sit up, and was so weak she could hardly talk, but she checked their fingernails and made sure they had brushed their teeth. When they came home that day, she was in a coma. I told them she was asleep. I didn't let them say goodnight to her because she looked so awful and that scared the little ones pretty bad. The next morning when they left for school, she was still in a coma.

Well, Faith died about an hour later. I had called her parents, and they got there while the children were in school. By the time the kids got home for lunch, the undertaker had already come and gone. Ellen saw her grandparents and said, "Why are *they* here? What's happened?!" She was so scared she was yelling. I said, "Kids, your mother has died. And we've got to be glad because she won't suffer anymore." Well, that didn't wash at all. Partly because I broke up as I said it. Ellen screamed. Like an animal. Just screamed. The two boys began to cry. Her grandmother took Ellen into her arms and said something like, "God has taken her, and he loves her more than we can." But Ellen pounded against her and continued screaming. "No! God *doesn't* love her. If He did, he'd leave her with us. We need her *so much*! *I hate God!*" I am very religious and that hurt me. Ellen is now an adult, but she still isn't interested in God.

Beth's mother, quoted above, says,

The last year, since the whole thing, my husband and I . . . . It's been touch and go. We fight more now than we used to. We both understand why. One time he wants to talk about it, and I don't. The next I want to talk, and he doesn't. He hasn't missed once going to the cemetery. He has gone every single weekend. He takes Beth's dog with him. He is a loner. He bikes a lot, alone.

Not only is there gaping loneliness following the death of a loved one, but a thousand unwanted and many times unexpected emotions rush into the vacuum.

Many survivors find that they feel guilty. They remember times when they could have been more considerate, or when they could have listened more understandingly.

Or they feel anger. Family members report being inexplicably enraged against the one who died. A midwestern man, overwhelmed by debts and responsibilities with children, says he actually found himself saying out loud to his dead wife, "Yeah!

You got out of this, didn't you? Left *me* the whole mess, didn't you?!" More commonly, the survivor will take out her fury on doctors, since they failed to save the loved one. But many times the survivor feels a generalized, free floating anger at everyone and everything. A man whose wife died of melanoma said that for months he would "fly off the handle" at the slightest provocation.

Sometimes, if the person is religious, he will seethe at God for letting him down. A New Yorker says,

> Okay, I can understand suffering. You learn from it, right? But what good did it do *her*? She may have learned something, but then she died. What good does it do to learn? When you die?

A Canadian man still goes daily to his Roman Catholic church to pray for his dead wife. But his friends wonder why. Instead of finding solace in his faith, he is deeply bitter with the deity and the clergy who serve Him. A Jewish woman in the east whose husband died in a Catholic hospital says,

> I went to temple every Friday. I had the rabbi praying for Steve. All my friends, everyone. I even prayed to *that*. (Points to crucifix) *Anything* to save Steve. But nothing helped. Now I stay at home. I mean, what good does religion do?

Children are often so filled with anger they become surly, even disruptive in school. Or they become withdrawn and refuse to speak to others.

Sexual pressures may rise for those who lose a mate, especially for those who have small children. Most parents are reluctant to leave their lonely children for long or to bring a sexual partner to the home.

One middle-aged woman says she became a flirt, and promiscuous.

If the survivor is old, the loneliness can be devastating. A New Yorker insists on staying in the apartment he shared with his wife of more than fifty years. He putters around aimlessly, tries to write a book about his experiences, but is unable to concentrate. Meanwhile, his children, grown and living with their families in other states, worry about him constantly.

A Colorado CanSurmount coordinator tells the reaction of one woman to the loss of her husband.

I had a well established volunteer who went to see a patient, and he was dying. His wife made the statement to the volunteer, "As soon as he dies, I'm going home and kill myself." The volunteer came to me, I went to see the social worker, and he to the doctor. When the man died, the wife was put in the hospital as a patient.

All family members suffer when a loved one dies, but it is probably the children who suffer the most. A man who lost his young wife agonizes over this memory:

I couldn't afford a housekeeper, so my son and I batched. We lived only a block from school and he walked home for lunch. He was in the second grade then. If I'd forgotten to put anything out for him—and I did forget a lot, I'm afraid—he'd push a chair and climb up on the counter and get a jar of peanut butter down for a sandwich. One day he called me at the office and he was hysterical. He said, "Daddy, why am I always so lonely?"

Perhaps the most pathetic suffering is among handicapped children. Ray Bassett lost his wife, Frannie, a CanSurmount coordinator, to cancer of the lymph nodes. He says,

Our youngest child is handicapped. It's like autism. He is twenty-six now. He doesn't learn, doesn't really talk, can hardly hear anything either. I think all the time, when Frannie was sick, uh . . . . He lives at this house for handicapped people. He has a job, and he has to live in that controlled environment. He works forty hours a week and makes money and contributes toward his keep and stuff like that. He is the one I worry the most about. I tried to protect him, but what could I do? He was hurt the most. And he couldn't understand.

After Frannie died, he stayed home for awhile. The first thing he did, he went to her closet and took all her clothes out. Why he did that, I don't know. He cleaned out all the cupboards, took everything out and put them in a box. And when he went back to Bethel to live—he had pictures there of Frannie. A couple of weeks after the funeral, I went over there. The pictures of Frannie were down off the wall and in the closet. Sitting on the floor. I didn't know why. I tried to say something, and he just clammed up. But I discovered in talking to Frannie's brother, who is a psychologist, that this was part of his grieving. He just hurt too much to look at a picture.

# 9
# Dare To Be Vulnerable:
# The CanSurmount Volunteers

Volunteers have a hard time explaining just what it is they do that patients find so helpful. They say that most visits are "normal, chatty, interrupted conversations. You might just be a nice lady who stopped by and not be remembered again." But often there is important communication in a seemingly inconsequential contact. Charles Petet (a minister and one of the early advisors to CanSurmount) says:

> I have been told the volunteer will sometimes come out of a situation, feeling, "Boy, was that a waste of time!" But the next time they go in they discover they had said some magic phrase they didn't even remember that had made the patient's day.

An oncologist believes information is the chief gift to the patient. He says:

> CanSurmount is a valuable program. Because, as you know, we tell the patient what is going to happen to her from the scientific aspect of treatment. What her disease may or may not do. But there is so much we as physicians forget that the patients may experience that is scary to them. A CanSurmount volunteer may come around and visit some patient after we've told him what is going to happen and tell him twice what we can about what is *really* going to happen. The *nitty-gritty things*, which we as physicians, who have never experienced the treatment itself . . . the route the patient has to go. So it's a big help.

Patients do need more information. What is their treatment going to be like? Will it be painful? What will it do to their bodies, the quality of their lives? Will they be able to have children after the treatment? Will they be able to work as before? Darlene Silver, a long time volunteer at General Rose Medical Center in Denver, says,

> About fifty percent of the patients I have seen want more information about their cancer. They have gone through the denial, the anger, the acceptance. Now they want to get on with the treatment.

CanSurmount considers giving information so important that it sponsors programs for volunteers, patients and their families. And CanSurmount volunteers frequently refer patients to other self-help groups. Rachel Perlick, coordinator at Aurora Presbyterian and a double mastectomy patient herself, remembers such a time.

> A little eighty-five year old woman had a mastectomy. The nurse wanted me to see her. I went in and spent a half hour with the lady. You know what? She was concerned with filling the other side of her bra! She was eighty-five and she wanted to be feminine. People say, "Hey, she's eighty-five! Why should she care about losing a breast?" Some might not, but she did. I called Reach to Recovery and they showed her how to handle it.

Imparting information can be helpful to the stunned and confused patient or to family members. But it can also be a point of danger, and volunteers are carefully instructed how to handle requests. In a training session Bobby Colby said:

> If the patient brings up religion, and you're comfortable talking about it, wonderful. But don't bring it up. We're a non-sectarian organization. And about unproven methods of treatment, if someone asks you if you know where you can get laetrile, what you think about the Greek diet, or the macrobiotic diet, the coffee enemas, whatever, don't be horrified and say, "What are you? Some kind of nut?" Or, if you are a real believer yourself, don't talk about it with the patients. We are the American Cancer Society, and we believe in proven methods. Please, above all, be

non-judgmental! Just say, "Gee, I don't know much about that.
Have you asked your doctor?" If someone is packing his bags to go
to Tiajuana, there isn't anything you can do about it. But urge the
patient to discuss it with his doctor. Respect the patient's values.
Never give advice like, "Gee, I wouldn't take that kind of chemo.
It'll make your hair fall out." You can give *tips*, like, well,
"Methotrexate causes a terrible taste in your mouth. So, I'd carry
little red mints and suck on them." That's a tip.

An older oncologist, who was trained in the days when patients were told very little about their disease, says he has been
astounded at how much patients want to know. The days when
they were willing to remain ignorant are vanishing.

But it is not just facts about treatment, or even about handling financial or physical problems that the patient needs. He
needs to know how to handle his *feelings* and those of his family.
Kay Borvansky's story is an example. Kay is from Chicago, studied
for a time to become a nurse, then met and married a construction
worker and moved to Steamboat Springs. When her children were
five years and ten months old, she developed a melanoma of the
eye and was told it had to be removed. She and her family were
devastated. She describes one of the most difficult parts of her
experience:

> I was really put out about the fact that this was happening to me
> and there was no one I could really share it with. I mean, I shared
> it with my husband, and my whole family was really supportive,
> but there were things I needed to talk to someone about that they
> couldn't help me with. Some of the feelings, the fears. I wanted
> someone who had been through a similar situation to say to me,
> "It's going to be okay," or, "This is what you've got to do."

While Kay waited for her surgery, she expressed her wish to
talk to someone, and a friend found another young woman who
had lost an eye to melanoma. Kay remembers:

> I went and had lunch with this girl, and we connected
> immediately. She shared a lot of the same feelings I was
> experiencing. She said the same thing, if she'd have had someone
> to talk to before surgery, she'd have understood a little better where
> she stood. That kind of stuff. It had been five years for her.

That was real good for me. I heard things I didn't want to hear. You know? As far as wearing a prosthesis and what you have to do with it and all that kind of stuff. But it was something I needed to know. It was a real hard time for me, but she really helped me get through it.

Since the volunteer knows what feelings are coursing through the patient, she can sometimes help the patient and family members to begin talking. Denise Gibson, a Hodgkin's patient, and one of the first volunteers, says:

Very often I would go out in the evenings and families would be there. A number of times my being there and talking with the patient, asking questions, would start a dialogue that obviously had never existed before. The family found out the patient's feelings and the patient found out the family's. They talked to each other through me about things they hadn't been able to open up about before—fears, death, hopes, concerns. Many times there was an incredibly loving relationship, but it was like there was a wall that was created by the disease.

And this imparting of information may help to rid cancer of its stigma. One of the aims of CanSurmount is enabling people to discuss cancer. Paul Hamilton calls CanSurmount a "conspiracy" of cancer patients against the world. It is a "conspiracy" to induce people to listen, to learn and to give support. CanSurmount members speak to the public whenever possible. They appear on TV programs and lecture at colleges. They button-hole neighbors and tell them what it is like to be stricken with cancer. They even confront doctors.

In a conversation about the "detachment" of health care professionals, Kay Borvansky says, "We're trying to change all that." Asked *how* she intends to do so, she replies, "We're trying to drag doctors into groups like this, let them see how CanSurmount works. We'll even corner them at the meeting and say, 'Look, one of the things we lack the most is your *concern*. I wish you'd been more caring, or told me such and such.'"

Knowing what one is dealing with is a way of regaining control over one's life. Ignorance is helplessness. Knowledge is power. The more the patient knows about his disease, its implications for his future, and the kinds of treatment available, the more he can feel he is again directing his own life. Uncharitable persons have suggested that the reason some doctors don't want the patient to know anything is to keep the patient docile, more willing to obey the physician meekly. The doctors who use and appreciate Can-Surmount want their patients to know as much as the patients are willing to accept. They *want* them to make decisions for them-selves (with the advice of the physician, of course), to take more responsibility for what happens to them.

Dr. Eduardo Pajon, a young oncologist and a strong sup-porter of CanSurmount, says,

> It helps the patient have a little bit more control over his life. A lot of people feel that they lose that control when they get a diagnosis of cancer. I think CanSurmount gives them an area where they can air their feelings and become more open about it. It gives the patient more self assurance, so he can go back to his physician and become part of the treatment team. He can feel he is participating instead of being passive about it.

We have seen how Sid Kline cheerfully defied her doctors and went on a furlough from chemotherapy. It can be argued that she might have lived longer had she stuck with the treatment pre-scribed. But survival for twenty-four years with active, metastatic breast cancer is strong evidence of the wisdom of her decision. Taking charge of her life, becoming responsible for her treatment, may actually have contributed to Sid's long survival. Her body may have been telling her something no physician could know. At the very least, it gave her a sense of dignity. She wasn't a thing manipulated by doctors. She was using her doctors as health ad-visors, not being used by them. Certainly her actions added to the *quality* of her life. Sid Kline, for one, needed respite from the vigorous therapy.

Dorothy Kubitschek, a long time Denver volunteer, was stricken with a malignant lymphoma and was treated by radiation. She says,

> I think the neatest thing about CanSurmount is that they stress the quality of life, over even the quantity of life. I think that is an important concept. Do you know LaMarr Bomareto? She is the most wonderful person. Such an encouragement to people. So positive. We have talked about this many times, and we value

quality much more than quantity of life. She says, "I don't want them to do anything to take away the quality of my life." It depends on the person. There are a lot of people who want all the medicine they can get. I think our society is raised that way. You know? Go to the doctor, he'll make you well. I don't believe that. I think you use your doctor like a tool. A help to make yourself well.

This does not mean that CanSurmount urges people to become their own doctors. The vast majority do exactly what the physician recommends. But each knows that in the final analysis it is his life and that he must make the decisions. A cancer patient must sometimes decide if he will take the risk of having only one testicle removed when the physician recommends that both be taken. One woman refused to have chemicals injected into her spinal column. Another decided to try an experimental procedure which involved destroying all her bone marrow. Some patients had died as a result of the treatment, but she survived and was cured. CanSurmount recognizes that any patient wishing to make such decisions must have information.

And while volunteers are carefully trained not to criticize a doctor or challenge the treatment he has prescribed, they will urge the patient to stand up for his rights. Kay Borvansky says:

A lot of times patients come to our meetings and they're really frustrated, because they feel the doctor didn't answer a question. A bunch of people pipe up and say, "Now wait just a minute!" These people, they've been through it, you know? So they say, "You go back in there and tell him you want to know. You're the one who's paying the bill. He's supposed to take care of you. You have every right to ask him things." They give that person the courage to talk with the doctor. Then, if the doctor still doesn't take care of them, they have the courage to walk, get another doctor. The people in CanSurmount are your backbone. They're the ones who're always telling you what your rights are because they've been there.

In training sessions volunteers are warned that some patients quickly become dependent and want to use them as personal servants. It is easy for a volunteer to be so sympathetic that he finds himself running errands, locating a housekeeper or acting as a chauffeur. That must be avoided because volunteers would soon be worn out and because patients must learn to handle their own, changed lives.

Volunteers groping for words to describe their contribution often come up with something like, "being a friend." Dorothy Kubitschek says drily, "There aren't many people who want to sit down and have a light hearted conversation about cancer."

Andy Bryant, one of the first men to volunteer, says,

> I think the main thing we did for patients was to take away the isolation. Let them know they're not alone. You feel so lonely.

A young man who had a form of malignant lymphoma re-members:

> I consider myself strong, but I'm human. I just wanted to talk to somebody, the night before I got chemotherapy. There were a lot of times I tried to reach out, and there was nobody to reach to. Now that's all changed. I know the organization of CanSurmount. I know how to reach out.

Even when one's friends do rally and try to provide support for the cancer patient during his long ordeal, it may not be the kind he needs. The same young man says:

> When you have cancer, sometimes you don't feel like being around healthy people. I mean, the cheery, happy little families where everything is going just fine. My wife and I wanted to be around other people like us. I guess misery loves company.

More likely, what the cancer patient misses is the under-standing others in his plight provide. CanSurmount members know a thousand little things that healthy people and health care professionals do (often inadvertently, unintentionally) that deepen the isolation of the patient. In a training session, Shirley Jenkins, coordinator at Presbyterian Medical Center in Denver, advised new volunteers:

> Never stand over a patient and look down on him. Pull up a chair and get as close to eye level as possible. Patients look up at everybody, the doctors, the nurses. People don't like to be looked down to. Even sit on the bed—if you have permission first.

Many times a lasting friendship is formed. Helen Singer, another of the early members of CanSurmount, continues as a volunteer in Paul Hamilton's office. Asked just what it is she gives to patients, she shakes her head and says:

> What do we give? One patient said, "I've made a friend while I'm
> in this deplorable condition." That was nice. I don't know, maybe
> it's friendship. That is a lot. People are very vulnerable when
> they're trapped in that hospital bed. I really think if that's all, it's
> worth it.

She is silent for awhile, remembering the people she has known during her years with CanSurmount. Then she says,

> We had one man who couldn't speak. It was so frustrating to him.
> His wife, his whole family was very attentive. But . . . . That was
> one of the cases where it took all the courage I had to walk in that
> room.
>  At first the family just sort of looked at me, and I was afraid I was
> intruding. But each time I was told to go back. Eventually, the wife
> relaxed and talked to us about this incredible problem. She had to
> just watch him go, and it was very, very miserable. She had gone
> to work at a store downtown to make ends meet. I would go have
> lunch with her. Even after he died. She needed to talk to someone.

Occasionally, the friendships have amusing consequences. One strong volunteer tells this story with a twinkle in her eye:

> I was seeing a lady. I had gotten out of touch with her for about
> two weeks. The last time I had talked to her, she told me she was
> feeling better. About three weeks went by, and I called the house to
> talk to her. A gentleman answered the phone. I asked for her, and
> he said, "She's not here." I said, "Would you please tell her I
> called." He said, "That's going to be kind of hard to do, because
> she's dead." I said, "I beg your pardon!?" He said, "She died last
> Thursday." I said I was sorry and explained who I was. He said,
> "I'm her husband, and I remember that she talked about you. She
> said you were a good friend to her. Will you come be my friend,
> too?"

But perhaps more important than friendship is the hope the

volunteer brings. A man in his early middle years was suddenly stricken with cancer. He tells of the hour he spent with the doctor, hearing about the extensive surgery he had to endure, the radiation and chemotherapy that would follow. Then he was admitted to the hospital, a vigorous active man, successful in business, an avid participant in sports, now crushed by what he had been told. He knew nothing about cancer except that most people who got it died of it. He says he anticipated nothing but endless, painful therapy, then a lingering death. But as he lay in the bed, there was a knock on the door and a lovely young woman entered. She said, "Hello. I'm a patient, too, and I thought I'd drop in to say hello." She told him that five years before she had the same kind of cancer, her treatment had been the same, and she had fully recovered. The man remembers with awe, "My God! She was an angel sent by God!"

A nurse who has watched CanSurmount from its inception says: "CanSurmount is very, very useful. When people can see someone who is cured, or is in remission, it gives them hope." A volunteer agrees, "CanSurmount lets people who've just been diagnosed know that cancer is not necessarily the kiss of death." And another:

> We give people visible evidence that they can get well. We don't know if they *will*, but at least here's somebody that did. I mean, "She's gone back to work. It's seven years later and gee, she looks wonderful. I'm losing my hair, but she lost hers too, and look how pretty her hair looks now." It's not in a book or on a TV screen. It's not fantasy. It's a real person who comes in and shakes hands with you or hugs you. We people who have been through the cancer experience are for others the light at the end of the tunnel.

Sometimes the reassurance the volunteer gives is not only that of survival, but of a normal life. A Canadian coordinator gives a poignant example:

> There are a lot of men with testicular cancer these days. We try to send a young volunteer who has had testicular cancer. This particular volunteer I am thinking of has even produced a child, so he's a success story. It's a real upper for a patient to be seen by somebody like that.

The encouragement the victim receives can have dramatic results. A volunteer remembers one such case:

> This one man was just about catatonic when he came, withdrawn, curled up, didn't say anything. His cancer had devastated him. But before the end of the meeting, he was contributing, beginning to live again. He was even inviting people over to his house. I think if you can make a person believe there is life after cancer, that you can enjoy it, that's the most important thing CanSurmount does. I'd hate to think I'd have another experience with cancer and CanSurmount wouldn't be there for me.

Another contribution volunteers can make, to family members as well as to patients, is to inspire courage. And as poet Robinson Jeffers has said, "There is no substitute for courage!"

Frequently, the terror at being diagnosed is so overwhelming that the patient will become withdrawn, like the man described above. Many patients simply want to get the dying over with. But if the patient can meet a person who has been through a similar experience, and who has met the challenge with courage and determination, he can be inspired to fight, too. Some volunteers believe this is the most important thing they do for the patient.

Bobby Colby had not been visited by a volunteer during her hospitalization or convalescence. But the story of her first CanSurmount meeting is worth repeating.

> My doctor was the one who brought it up. He asked if I'd ever heard of CanSurmount. I said, "No." He said he thought it might be good for me and something I would do well at. I must say my first impressions of, well, what I had in mind, a club of cancer patients, was not something that was the most appealing thing in the world. Plus, I've never been a joiner, a coffee clutcher. I thought, "I don't know if this is going to be my cup of tea."
>
> But when I went to the first meeting in October of '78 there was a gal in my session who'd had a mastectomy, a hysterectomy, a colostomy and an ileostomy. Over an eighteen year period. Lord! She was gorgeous! In her early fifties, full of life and looking as if she had stepped off the front cover of a Vogue Magazine. It was the first time I'd ever sat down with another cancer patient. When I walked away from that meeting, I thought, "If that gal can do it,

what's a little breast?" That was the start of my climb up out of the abyss of having cancer.

In a sense, courage is more important than hope because the cancer victim knows full well that he may not be one of the lucky ones. *His* cancer may not respond to therapy. He may face recurrences, additional vigorous treatment, even death.

A Mexican-American who was never himself a volunteer, shows how courage can improve the quality of life even if it does not increase longevity.

> I think CanSurmount is a good thing, you know? Some patients, they close their eyes. They feel so bad. But after you meet the CanSurmount people, they perk you up. Because them people have that sickness too, you see? I think you can tell them people things. It's okay! Then you feel better. I really think it is harder for my wife and kids. You know? Which one day it *will* be! But what the heck, you can go out there and be killed by a truck. There you go, you know? What scares people the most is the suffering thing, you know? After being in that hospital and having to have this taken out of you and that done to you, it gets pretty scary for some people. Well, for me too. I ain't that brave!

One volunteer who perfectly displayed the courage needed to surmount cancer's challenge, and who then devoted himself to instilling that courage in others was Jack Shigetomi. Jack was blade thin and bent from his long battle, but he had an indomitable spirit. He was born in Colorado of first generation Japanese immigrants. When World War II came he and his entire family were imprisoned in one of America's detention camps. But Jack Shigetomi never surrendered to bitterness. Instead, he volunteered to serve in the nation's armed services and became a noncommissioned officer in the famous Go For Broke battalion which fought so heroically in Italy. Three times he was decorated. First, he was awarded the Bronze Star for saving the life of a lieutenant who had been wounded and was caught between the lines. Next came the Purple Heart. Shigetomi's platoon was caught in withering machine gun fire, and he crawled forward to knock out the gun. He succeeded but was badly wounded by shrapnel. One piece tore open his liver; another passed through his stomach and lodged in his heart. Carried to the rear, he was inspected in triage. The doctor decided there was no hope and left him to die. But as Jack said later, "I preferred living." The tough little man clung to life until, finally, a colonel saw that alone of those left in triage Shigetomi was still alive. Surgery was performed and while he recovered in an army hospital General Mark Clark presented him a Silver Star for heroism.

After the war Jack became a salesman. Near the end of his life, while he sucked on oxygen, he said ebulliently, "I love to sell! Love it! Love to meet new people, see new places!" His old wounds bothered him all his life, and he developed osteoporosis. But nothing stopped him from a vigorous life. Until cancer. Yet for fourteen years he fought that with as much courage and determination as he had everything in life, never losing his marvelous sense of humor. He was a "natural" for CanSurmount.

When they started this CanSurmount I was already there! I find that if the families wouldn't baby the patients, you know? yield to them? I think there'd be a lot more of us who wouldn't be going down the rough trail. A lot more of us *saved!* Because, cancer can put you in a depression feeling. Then you get worse. You ain't got nothing there to fight with!

This one guy, he had just gotten Hodgkin's. Just the starting of it. That's the time to catch it! But he was going downhill right away. His wife asked me to talk to him. So I went down there, but he didn't want to listen. He said, "You've never had to cope with this, so you don't know what it's like." I told him I was a patient, too, but he wouldn't listen. Wouldn't take his treatments or nothing. Just gave up. Boy, it wasn't long before, bingo! He was gone!

I got *compassion*. I don't feel good if I can't do something for somebody.

A lot of people, they get so mad and they say, "Why me?" I say, "What do you mean, 'why me?' I don't care if you're a millionaire or what, if it's your turn to get that, you're going to get it. It's like a cold or anything else. It just hits. I always say, "Hey, that's life! There's always room for one more problem!" The minute you start feeling sorry for yourself, that's when the trouble starts! Oh, I can tell you! You can get it by the bucket full!

This one fellow I knew, he committed suicide in the hospital. He just convinced himself that he was terminal. That's the worst thing you can do, think you're terminal! A little hope, just one breath! That's all you need! Keep on going. Too many people die in bed! I'm going to get up and enjoy life as long as I can. I just cast a low silhouette and keep going!

Jack did keep going. He visited patients in the hospital when he was so sick himself that he could hardly walk. He padded about giving courage and challenging patients to fight their disease when they were too tired or discouraged to try. When he was finally confined to his own home, he moved his bed to the living room so he could be "part of things." But time ran out on this cheerful, energetic warrior. In August of 1984 Jack turned off the television set and went to sleep. He never woke up. Dozens of people attest to how much he helped them believe in life again, despite having cancer. He did, indeed, have compassion.

Jack Shigetomi was the perfect example of what Jean Tuthill, a coordinator in Presbyterian Medical Center, meant when she said,

> I think the theory of CanSurmount, that you can *surmount* your illness, stay on top, be strong enough, and courageous enough not to let yourself go under emotionally, psychologically, or be defeatist, is good.

That courage improves the quality of life is beyond dispute. Whether it does more is controversial. Certainly, there are whining, self-pitying people who have survived cancer and courageous people who have perished. Yet, few physicians doubt the importance of courageous resolution. Dr. Robert Berris, a distinguished oncologist and one of the early supporters of CanSurmount, is skeptical of all psychological theories of cancer's origin. But he admits,

> One study, which I don't think has ever been repeated, but is often quoted, indicated that the feisty patient was the patient who lived longer, on any given cancer ward. That may indeed be true. I don't know. But we're *all* acquainted with the patient who is going to live until Christmas or until their grandbaby is born, and so on, and indeed they do and indeed soon thereafter die. A lot of people go through here, getting chemotherapy, for instance, and I can kind of spot the ones who are going to have a tough time with it and the ones who are going to bear with it easy. The burly tough old

church-going lady usually doesn't have much trouble with her chemotherapy. But the young society matron has a bad time of it. The first one knows this is a tough world. The second kind thinks the world is supposed to bow to her will. When it doesn't, she has a tough time.

Certainly, most CanSurmount volunteers believe in the power of determination. They admit its limits but think it helps. John Burgess, a Hodgkin's victim, CanSurmount volunteer and captain in the air force, says:

> In the cancer ward I met some young men my age who had given up on life. They rolled over like puppy dogs, and the nurses were scratching them. They were doing everything for them. I saw them die. I tell patients today, without being too hard on them, I say, "It is those *fighters*, not just the ones who get up and scream and yell, but the ones who want to take back the control they lost, they're the ones who live!"

Vicky Gorman, a young mother who survived breast cancer, tells of the first day after her surgery.

> The next morning this kind lady (Rachel Perlick, a CanSurmount coordinator) came over and held my hand and was with me. I had two aunts who both died at the age of thirty-three and left small children. I thought, 'I am repeating this, and I just *can't!*' I had seen how hurt their families were. I wasn't really afraid of death, but I didn't want to leave that hurt for my children, that loneliness. I was determined to be a fighter!

Families of cancer patients need to have their courage re-stored, too. Peggy Pugsley, whose husband died of prostatic cancer, says,

> CanSurmount is so important because under such a stressful time if people don't receive the proper back-up, they might become bitter, lash out, be hostile. But in talking about it, sharing it, well . . . . I know I used to feel so tired and discouraged and down and out, and then I'd visit with one of them and I'd think, "Gee! If *they* can do it, *I* can too." Sometimes it was just little things. I'd be in his room, exhausted, discouraged. Then a CanSurmount person

would come in and I'd go out and have a cup of coffee in the lounge with them. When it came time to go back in his room, I was fortified.

But if the volunteers were there only to goad the patient and family members into fighting harder, they would be providing a minimal service. For many patients are going to die, many families will lose a loved one. They need comfort more than stern admonitions to keep a stiff upper lip. Life, after all, is difficult under the best of circumstances, and when one has cancer, it is agonizingly hard. As one philosopher phrased it, life is always fatal. The Psalmist compares human beings to the grass. "In the morning it flourisheth, and groweth up; in the evening it is cut down, and withereth." In addition to calls to courage, we need comfort to face harsh realities.

It's astonishing to new cancer victims how few people even try to be comforting, or how ineffectual they are if they do try. One of the things cancer patients yearn for, and seldom receive, is touching. Lewis Thomas is speaking for all sick people, certainly for cancer patients, when he says:

> Some people don't like being handled by others, but not, or almost
> never, sick people. They *need* being touched, and part of the
> dismay of being very sick is the lack of close human contact.
> Ordinary people, even close friends, even family members, tend to
> stay away from the very sick, touching them as infrequently as
> possible for fear of interfering, or catching the illness, or just for
> fear of bad luck.

Patients have wept as they told how they longed to be hugged, kissed, stroked. But the revulsion people feel for the disease seems to be transferred to the patient. So, one of the most valuable services the volunteer performs is touching the patient— and thereby showing others that it is all right to do the same. Bobby Colby gave this instruction in a training session:

> You go over and give the patient a hug or kiss or something, and
> the patient will say, "You're the first person that has touched me in
> two weeks." We start feeling when we're diagnosed that nobody
> wants to touch us, we're not beautiful enough. We aren't worthy of

that. Just holding the hand, a kiss on the cheek, a pat, whatever. It makes a person feel so much better.

In the same session this interchange occurred between Shirley Jenkins and Bobby:

SHIRLEY: The young lady was very ill, and did in fact die that day. Her family members were sitting there in their chairs. I had met some of them. Others I hadn't met. I said "Hello" to the one I knew and walked right over to the bed. I bent down and kissed the woman and said, "I love you. We're here with you." I don't know if she heard me or not. Then I just sat there for awhile, holding her hand.

BOBBY: God! You can help people *so much*, just letting yourself do that. Many times a family member will be *afraid* to touch someone. They're afraid they'll *hurt* them in some way. Or they don't know if they *should*. Go over and give that person a hug or squeeze. Family members will likely say to themselves, "Hmmmph! If *you* can do that, so can I." I don't know how many times I have walked back a couple of days later and found a family member there holding the hand, giving them a smooch, arm around, whatever.

One of the loneliest places in the world is a Veteran's Administration Hospital. Many of the patients are indigents, many are old men with no families. Richard Walker, who was an officer in the army during the war in Viet Nam, calls regularly at Denver's V.A. Hospital. He says:

I've had some really positive experiences with people, and I don't think they were blowing smoke. It really did mean a lot to them. At first some of the older guys would get this look in their eye, like, "Don't give me any B.S.! You don't look like anyone who has had cancer." But once they realize that you have undergone surgery and chemo and the whole bit, they stop and listen. Or they are suddenly more willing to relate what their real fears are. In many cases they don't have anybody around they can just kind of let their hair down with and say that they're really scared about what is going to happen.

And when the time comes, as it does for many cancer patients, that remissions are past, the weary body can no longer fight, and death is close, the CanSurmount volunteer can perhaps be the most helpful. She has herself had to face the possibility of death; in some cases the volunteer is visiting others even as her own life is coming to an end. The two, volunteer and patient, can find peace by sharing their fears, exulting in the good memories they have of better days, and sympathizing with each other. Even though volunteers emphasize the importance of fighting for life, they recognize that there comes a time when fighting is futile. Kay Borvansky put the case well:

> If people are terminal and they're going to die, they need to know it's *okay* to die. They've tried the best they can, and they have the right to quit. They're not failing themselves or anyone else.

And when the fight is finally over for the patient, the family begins a new ordeal—of grief. Some, who had received so much comfort from CanSurmount, wonder if they will now be left to face the aftermath alone. Peggy Raffin says:

> The people at CanSurmount have been through it all and can guide you back. Put you back on the path, with love and support. When you hurt *so much*, you want *somebody* to *understand*. And they know. They have been there. But you wonder if they'll *continue* to love you, after it's over, and they do. They're right there even now, just when I reach the bottom.

It may seem odd to some, but the way volunteers give courage, comfort and peace is not by delivering lectures. They do it mostly by *listening*. There is no dearth of people to advise the patient. Doctors and clergymen readily tell the patient how she *ought* to feel. Psychologists and social workers advise him how to deal with his emotions. But few listen. However, volunteers remember how they yearned for somebody to listen to them, instead of instruct or advise. Rachel Perlick says,

> Somebody asked me once, "What is it you really do?" I said, "I think probably the biggest thing I do is listen and hold somebody's hand." This person said, "Don't put yourself down like that." Boy, did I get upset! I said, "That's not putting myself down. Being a

good listener is not an easy task." I mean, some people are boring, some people are not your type. We all know we have the answer to how they *should* deal with this, and we all want to say, "Do this, do that." But that's not what we're all about. We're there to *listen*, to be supportive, to say we understand, even to hold their hand.

Of course, not everyone wants to talk. Some are too depressed, and some are simply private. That wish to be left alone is honored. But Jesse Bischoff, a coordinator in Colorado Springs, tells this moving story:

> A lot of folks *think* they don't want to talk about it. They start out kind of reluctantly, or they start out saying, "I promised myself I wouldn't cry." They're so afraid. They think they have to keep up a facade. There was a patient who said, "The nurse told me you were coming, and I went out for a walk. I was hoping I would miss you." I said, "Don't you feel like talking?" She said, "Well, not really. But you've had cancer, so maybe it's all right." She proceeded to talk non-stop for over an hour.

One of the most common statements by people who have been visited by CanSurmount is that the volunteers show such love. This cynical generation is always suspicious of such statements. Is it possible to love someone we have never met before? Someone who is perhaps angry, whimpering with self pity, or who may smell bad? Is it possible to love someone with whom we would normally feel no congeniality? It seems an overstatement to describe the "transaction" between volunteer and patient as love. And in a sense it is not love, if we mean the kind of feelings we have for members of our own family or personal friends. But there is another kind of love, of which Jesus spoke, when he said that we are to love our neighbors as ourselves. He surely did not mean *liking* a person or even feeling warm toward the person. Most probably what He meant was *caring* about the welfare of that person, wishing him well, even doing what we can to insure the other's safety and happiness. It is this kind of love the volunteer gives, and it is magic in its effect.

Richard Walker talks about his visits at the V.A. Hospital:

> What we're all really hoping for is a certain amount of human warmth. Just a—real relationship. Somebody who's there because

they want to be. It's not a job. These old guys are always quite surprised. They ask, "How often do you come up? Is this your regular job?" I have to tell them a couple of times, "No, this is totally volunteer."

It's no wonder patients are surprised. We live in a time when everything is left to professionals who are paid for their services and who are not necessarily thought of as caring people. It is expected that everyone has an "angle," and "is out for himself." That attitude makes for a lonely world, and when we are sick, even dying, such a world becomes intolerable. To look up from our bed and find no one who cares among those staring down at us, is to know ultimate loneliness. It is no wonder the CanSurmount volunteer can bring peace and courage when others cannot. The power of knowing that someone cares is seen in this statement by a woman whose daughter died on the cancer ward at Presbyterian Medical Center in Denver.

My first contact with CanSurmount was up on B-2. First, the welcome, from the nurses! Regina Schmitt and Chris Trani. All of them. The tender loving care they gave, so personal. The volunteer I met that day was wonderful. An older woman with leukemia herself. We became dear friends. She visited my daughter once a week, then in the lounge she talked with me and my husband so much. As things got worse and worse, they were all right there to glue me back together. The love that's on that floor, from the nurses, as well as the CanSurmount volunteers, that deserves a book!

And Shirley Jenkins remembers:

Paul had a young patient, in her twenties or early thirties. She had two small children, was divorced, parents lived in another state. We became acquainted with this girl, and when her disease had metastasized to her brain, and she knew it was going to be fast, she told us, shared it with us. She came into the hospital for the last time on a Thursday. She was very sick, and we knew this was the day she would die. In her room was a close friend, her mother, Sid Kline, Paul Hamilton and myself. The five of us were . . . one was holding her hand, another holding her foot. Another had a hand on her shoulder. We were all standing around her bed when she died. For her to know that we were all there, all the people who had become close to her in her illness, it was like, "Okay, I can die now." Dr. Hamilton took her hand to check her pulse. As we stood there, weepy-eyed, he looked down at her and walked to the foot of the bed and stood there with head lowered in prayer. Then he walked out of the room. I thought it was the most beautiful sight I've ever seen.

When a cancer patient becomes a volunteer and identifies with a newly diagnosed patient, he risks awakening his own bitter memories and half-buried fears. Yet, the volunteer knows that *not* to identify, not to care, is to refuse the patient the one thing he needs most.

As we have seen, people can almost always sense a lack of genuine concern and be hurt by it. Therefore, if a person becomes a CanSurmount volunteer, she *must* care, she *must* take up the burden of the other's pain. She must dare to be vulnerable.

And it is the willingness to be vulnerable that makes CanSurmount so magical. Offering oneself up to this kind of pain is the last and most important gift CanSurmount gives. It is a strange paradox that for the volunteer to make himself vulnerable to the pain the patient feels is to communicate strength to that person. Others can speak the same words, make the same gestures, use the same intonations, but if the patient senses that the other does not *feel his pain*, the words fall flat, the gestures are futile, the intonations are perceived as false.

Shirley Jenkins says,

Every time I think I can't take another week of this, I get a letter or a bouquet of flowers, or a phone call: "You were there when I needed you." It's worth it. All the pain.

The CanSurmount volunteer is the person Henri Nouwen described:

. . . when we honestly ask ourselves which persons in our lives mean the most to us, we often find that it those who, instead of giving much advice, solutions, or cures, have chosen rather to share our pain and touch our wounds with a gentle and tender hand. The friend who can be silent with us in a moment of despair or confusion, who can stay with us in an hour of grief and bereavement, who can tolerate not-knowing, not-curing, not-healing, and face us with the reality of our powerlessness, that is the friend who cares.

# 10
# I Would Never, Ever Trade It

The whole cancer experience, I must say, and you will probably hear this from other people, too—I would never, ever trade it for any other experience in my life. It taught me a lot. I grew up very rapidly. I would not want to go through it again. I become frightened every time I think it might happen again. But the experience was quite fantastic. I didn't know what kind of person I was until I went through that. I didn't know what my personality was, my thoughts, or ambitions or anything. But afterwards I had some very strong feelings, beliefs. I became much more mature. I found I couldn't relate to my friends in high school after the cancer—boys, girls, anyone.

College was better, but somewhat the same. I had an insight that nobody else had. Many of my friends, in college, the ones who became really close, understood that something had happened to me that they would never experience and that because of it, I am a different kind of person. It wasn't like I had any kind of Holier than Thou attitude, but I knew what I wanted. And what I didn't want. What the secret is, some would simply call maturity. But it is more maturity than most people ever achieve. I think my personality became very strong. A lot of people didn't know how to take it. Some people still describe me as aloof. I do stand back, think a lot. I am cautious, because I value my life. I value who I am since my

experience. I don't ever want to be shattered again. I don't want
anything to happen to make me different from the way I am now. I
like the way I am.

You know, that night I tried to kill myself? After surgery. Well, I
saw images, felt feelings, and I *felt* something or someone who
knows. I felt the pull, the feeling of someone saying, "You can't do
this. You're too young. You've got a lot of life left, blah, blah,
blah." Some ethereal type of sentences and words. I sat up in bed.
I don't know if I came close to death or not, but in my mind I had.
I wanted to die. Whatever it was, something popped me out of it.

After that I realized that I did want to live and wanted to make
the best of my life. For awhile I didn't know if it was God or what.
But it was interesting. For ten years after that. . . . You know, the
cure time for Hodgkin's is ten years. If you get through those ten
years, they say you're sure. I had very strong religious beliefs about
an entity. I didn't go to church. I didn't believe in the stuff that any
minister or priest kept telling me. I thought I knew more than they
did. But I believe in some sort of influence on my life.

Well, for those ten years I was, uh, I kind of laugh at this, and I
did in those ten years, but everything was so easy for me. I mean,
*everything*. So easy! I got jobs when I needed them, I had lots of
friends, I traveled. It just all kind of fell into place at the right time
and place.

Came the ten years and it was real strange. I was back in
Colorado. That summer, I was at a jazz festival in Telluride with
some friends, and it was a real nice summer. The festival was three
days long and I had planned on this little celebration. I had
brought up some champagne and glasses for my friends to help me
celebrate. That day I felt so good about getting to this point, and
there was this nice jazz music, and it was a beautiful day up in the
mountains. It was just real, real nice. I offered everybody a little
glass of champagne, to help me celebrate my ten years, and these
were the real understanding friends.

I went walking off then, out of the crowd, and I suddenly got this
funny feeling that I was being talked to. That somebody or
something was telling me something. I tried to listen, or key into
what it was. I thought, "Oh, you're just imagining things." But
whatever this was kept telling me, in effect, "Your ten years are up.
I have protected you all this time. Now it's time for you to live on
your own." I felt this veil, sort of, you know, lift off me. I felt as if

I had been living in a cocoon for ten years and it lifted off. I felt as if I were standing naked in the middle of this jazz festival.

After that I had all kinds of things happen, that I had to cope with, that I had never had before. Losing friends, people dying that had been close to me. Things just not going right for a long period of time. For about a month I was real angry because . . . I didn't know if I had brought this on myself or what. I felt so vulnerable. I wanted another ten years like those that were gone. But something had left, and now I had to battle the world on my own.

Now it's just life.

Not many cancer patients can tell a story as dramatic as Germaine Fraley's. But many patients do speak of having learned a secret about life. Sometimes their statements are astonishing. Betty Rollin was a TV news reporter who lost a breast to cancer. She was devastated. As we have said above, she left her first husband, went to live with another man, left him. Caught in the swirl of emotions that so often afflict people who have a brush with a life threatening disease, she wrote *First You Cry*, widely acclaimed for its honest and accurate description of the way cancer patients feel. The book gives the impression that this bright but emotionally immature woman was crushed by her encounter with cancer. However, five years later, she wrote a follow-up article for The New York *Times* Magazine. One immediately senses that Betty Rollin has become a different person. She has won a victory and broken through into a new kind of life. Ms. Rollin makes this startling statement:

> Five years ago, I felt sorry for myself that I could no longer keep a strapless dress up. Today I feel that losing a breast saved my life, and wasn't I lucky. And when I think of all the other good things that have come from that loss, I just look at that flat place on my body and think: small price.

Then, in discussing the possibility of a recurrence, she makes an even more stunning declaration.

> . . . I'm sure I won't be a good sport about it, especially if my life is cut short. But even if it is, I will look back at the years since the surgery and know I got the best from them. And I will be forced to admit that the disease that is ending my life is the very thing that made it so good.

Many cancer patients, and virtually all those who have become CanSurmount volunteers, claim much the same thing. Dorothy Kubitschek says calmly:

> When you visit cancer patients you get to know which ones are going to make it and which ones aren't. It's hard to visit with one who you're pretty sure is not. But, if you can say to them, "It's okay, either way," I think that gives them some peace of mind. I have come to that conclusion myself. If I stay well, that's fine. But if I don't, that's okay too. That is a hard thing to get yourself to say. But once you can, you have peace of mind. It's tremendous strength. I would not trade that sense for anything.

What is this secret the young Hodgkin's patient found? And how could Betty Rollin think that finding it was worth losing a breast? What is so powerful that Dorothy Kubitschek can say she can face death with tranquility? How can strength come from knowing how vulnerable we are? What courage can come from terror? What wisdom is seemingly given as compensation for the experience of cancer? What change has taken place in the person who has experienced it? As the young woman cited above says, she became more mature. That maturity has been won through struggle, and is a treasure worth sacrifice.

One is reminded of a young man so appalled by the Viet Nam war that he fled to Canada. When amnesty was granted by President Carter, he returned to the United States and was alarmed to find that those who had permitted themselves to be drafted had a maturity he lacked.

Any challenge, and especially an encounter with grim reality and even death offers maturity to those who will take it. Not the maturity of growing old, but genuine maturity: attaining new birth. Perhaps it can best be compared to the feeling one has on a difficult climb. The climber looks down and exults! To face a great challenge and survive can be exhilarating. One feels in command of himself. W.H. Murray expressed the sensation in this description of his expedition to the Himalayas.

> The hectic, bewildering weeks of preparation, the stupefying meals of the voyage out, the hustle at Bombay and bustle at Ranikhet—they were all like the wild waters of a subterranean stream, in the navigation of which we had been too busy to think. And now the

stream burst from its tunnel on to the open slopes of the Himalaya. It cast us out into sunshine. For a moment dazzled, we suddenly saw spread before us a world made new. All the senses of the soul were not so much refreshed as reborn, as though after death. We were free men once again, for the first time in months really able to live in the present moment.

The surviving cancer patient may feel as if she too, has been caught in "the wild waters of a subterranean stream," and swept helplessly toward annihilation. Then, miraculously, she is cast back into life, dazzled by its beauty, is reborn, free again, and able to live in the present moment. Bobby Colby says,

> If I could just bottle the feeling and give it to you, and all the folks you talk to! The feeling that everything is very precious and we're so lucky. Life is very, very beautiful.

Like so many others who have faced death and survived, Bobby is frustrated at being unable to communicate what she has learned.

> It's a sad thing! We have to wait until we have some sort of catastrophic news before we can really take a look at how fragile, how slight our time here on earth is. I tell young people, "Don't wait until a cancer diagnosis, or a heart attack smacks you in the face with your own mortality. I'm telling you, you're going to die. There's no way to escape it. Try to live every minute to the fullest, to do what will make you *really* happy in your life."
>
> So you say this, and the kids probably hear it and hang onto it for a minute or so. But they go out with their friends, and an hour or two later, they forget everything that you said. Until something terrible happens to them. How do you tell people, everything is precious, everything is fragile?

John Burgess says,

> When you come out of it, it's exciting. You look back at the valley out of which you climbed and you say, "I grew." I can't explain how I grew, but I am a better person, a different person. I feel I've done something others haven't done.

It must be said that many who endure the experience, even many who survive it, do not achieve that maturity. Cast out into a valley at the foot of the Himalayas, they may only curse the experience, and so busy themselves cleaning the mud from their clothes that they forget to lift their eyes and see Life rising before them in its majesty and beauty. We can only pity them. Cancer, like all tremendous experiences, *can* bring a new maturity. To suffer and *not* win the prize is tragedy.

The understanding a cancer patient may gain is really not a secret at all—it has been taught by religious leaders and philosophers through the ages. We have all heard the words, in our churches and synagogues, read them in books assigned by professors or perused for pleasure. But for most of us the seed fell on hard ground and did not take root. Something like an encounter with death may be required before we can appreciate what the sages have taught.

For example, one thing soon learned by cancer patients is not to be so concerned about the little things that bedevil us most of our lives. Jesus put it this way:

> Therefore I tell you, do not be anxious about your life, what you shall eat or what you shall drink, nor about your body, what you shall put on. Is not life more than food, and the body more than clothing? Look at the birds of the air: they neither sow nor reap nor gather into barns, and yet your heavenly Father feeds them. Are you not of more value than they? And which of you by being anxious can add one cubit to his span of life? And why are you anxious about clothing? Consider the lilies of the field, how they grow; they neither toil nor spin; yet I tell you, even Solomon in all his glory was not arrayed as one of these. But if God so clothes the grass of the field, which today is alive and tomorrow is thrown into the oven, will he not much more clothe you, O men of little faith? Therefore, do not be anxious, saying, "What shall we eat?" or "What shall we drink?" or "What shall we wear?"

One who has suffered pain and been torn by fear, who has seen how brief life can be, can appreciate this. CanSurmount volunteer Richard Walker says of his cancer experience:

> It was probably quite beneficial for me as a person. It changed a lot of things about the way I view life. For the first time, I learned how

to relax. I didn't have to be occupied with projects and work day in and day out. I learned to just sit for an hour or so, do some reading and just, relax. And I learned the importance of relationships with other people. I had always been pretty independent.

Bobby Colby describes how her life has changed:

I now read the books I want to read. I take time for myself. I have weeded out the negative folks in my life. I didn't do the dishes last night, but I sat down and wrote a girlfriend a letter I'd been wanting to write. I don't care that I could make twice the money out there someplace. We get by, the bills get paid. If there was anything in my life today that was making me unhappy, you'd best believe I wouldn't think twice about changing it. After cancer you know that new cars and that sort of thing are not what you want. I don't need a new wardrobe, a trip to Hawaii. Those things are nice, but there is so much more. More important.

Fears that once tormented people now leave them unimpressed. Betty Rollin put it well.

. . . when you're slightly afraid of death, you're less afraid of other things—e.g., bosses . . . Next to the Grim Reaper, how ferocious can even the most ferocious boss be?

Conflicts over trivial matters do not interest cancer patients much. Shirley Jenkins tells this story:

I had been at the hospital working all that day. Things were hard. A mother had lost her son, a woman lost her husband. I went to church that night, and they were having a business meeting. They were squabbling over some little thing. They looked at me and asked, "Don't you care?" I said, "I care. But after what I've been through this week, this is nothing. I'm sorry to feel this way, but that's the way it is."

Cancer patients who have faced death, and may have shorter than normal lives, do not want to spend their days worrying about things they have come to realize are inconsequential. Again, Betty Rollin:

I am less concerned about where my career is going. I don't know where it's going. I don't think about that. I think about where I am going and whether I like it.

One of the paradoxes of life is that most of us spend our time yearning for things which would do little for us. We want fame, wealth, power or luxury. Yet, attaining them may not solve the problems that annoy us. Cancer patients typically know that. For they have learned the beauty, the essence of life. They find the greatest joy is being able to return to work! It is tossing a child into the air, or seeing a son graduate from high school. Movies are made about people who hit the jack pot or commit a crime or fight a war. Headlines are made by glamorous, bejeweled rock-and-roll or movie stars who live in the fast lane. Who is interested in dull things like paying off mortgages or adding a patio to a home or taking the kids out for an ice cream cone? Yet the secret found by cancer patients is that *this* is what is important and lovely beyond the power of words to describe. Cancer patients typically lose interest in glamor and excitement. They find majesty in washing windows until they sparkle or snuggling down with a good book. They are interested less in the glittering lights of Las Vegas than in the shimmering light that suffuses their everyday life.

Kay Borvansky:

> People asked me, when you found you had this life threatening disease, what did you want to do? Did you feel like you wanted to travel, see the world? Go out and buy yourself a Cadillac? What did you want to do in case you should check out? I told them that all those things I'd always thought I wanted to do were totally insignificant.
>
> All I wanted to do was . . . well, the silliest thing—we were coming home from one of our visits to the doctor and everything was still kind of up in the air. I was having a hard time agreeing to surgery. I asked the doctor, "Why take out my eye? It's a perfectly good eye." He said, "Yes, and it is a perfectly good melanoma, too. Having that cancer in your eye is like having a rattlesnake in your living room. Conceivably, it might never bite. But then again, it might." But I just couldn't decide. I thought, 'Why not just hope the melanoma never does anything.' You know? 'Take the chance, let nature take its course.'

We stopped at Arthur Treacher's Fish and Chips, to get something to eat. Here I had this baby, and I was plunking him in the high chair and tying his bib on. And my other little boy was dropping his french fries all over the place during that meal. And the only thing I could think of was, a year from now I might not be here to do this. How stupid and insignificant this is, and how much I love it! I decided right then I wanted to go on doing that more than anything in the world.

I let them take my eye.

The author, Geoffrey Winthrop Young once observed, "We do not feel proud enough of being alive."

Of course, none of this is to say that cancer patients do not have all the day-to-day problems, all the irritations and frustrations that others have. As the months and years of a renewed health and normal life drift by, cancer patients tend to get caught up in dealing with those irritations, and the insight they have gained fades. Which is one of the reasons they become CanSurmount volunteers and return to the world of cancer. To be with others still fighting the battle with death, to share and to comfort helps volunteers retain their deep understanding of life.

Again, we may compare this to the feeling of those who have climbed great peaks. The poet, Eunice Tietjens, says,

> The stone grows old.
> Eternity is not for stones;
> But I shall go down from this airy space, this
>     swift white peace, this stinging exultation:
> And time will close about me, and my soul stir to
>     the rhythm of the daily round.
> Yet, having known, life will not press so close.
> And always I shall feel time ravel thin about me.
> For once I stood
> In the white windy presence of eternity.

Since so many CanSurmount volunteers have sensed that presence, they are fascinating people and fun to be with. A doctor, visiting a meeting of CanSurmount volunteers, says,

People who have had cancer, to me, are the most alive people there are. They are taking nothing for granted. Every single day is a gift.

You've faced your maker and come away from it. Everyone who has been told they have cancer knows the cards are on the table. This is no bullshit time. This is real stuff. The cancer is here and I've got to accept it and deal with it. I suppose that there are just as many people who have cancer who go home and sit in their house and brood. Fortunately, I don't see those people. The people I see at this meeting are some of the most vivacious I've ever met. To them life is serious business. I appreciate that. I think that is interesting. There are so many people in this world who are twenty- five years old and healthy and have a trust fund to live off who take life as a joke. I like people who take life seriously. Who look at it as a gift.

A Canadian volunteer tells this story:

We meet on a monthly basis. Then we have our guest speakers. They are in shock when they meet our people. As we introduce ourselves around the table and tell each other where we are with our cancer, the guest speakers are in shock. We had a psychologist speak to us only two months ago, and the first thing he said when he got up to speak was, "This group has absolutely blown my mind!" We are ever amazed at how little psychologists and other people in the "people field" know about cancer and about cancer patients.

A Colorado volunteer says with a smile,

I have come to the conclusion that only nice people get cancer. Because of our experience with CanSurmount. I have known so many really wonderful people there.

Not all cancer patients, of course, have come to this vision of life. And not all volunteers are radiant personalities. Despite efforts to use only those who are positive and kindly persons, some grumps or self-centered souls slip through the selection process. One cancer victim asked that a certain volunteer be kept from her room. The volunteer's mournful expression reminded her of "Digger O'Dell." CanSurmount is like any other organization, staffed by human beings who make mistakes. But it *is* amazing how many of the volunteers, even those who are still actively fighting their disease, are strong, kind and good natured.

It must also be admitted that they are not always perceived that way by others. For people who have been through such an experience and have grown so much are not always the docile patients preferred by some doctors. If they are no longer so afraid of their bosses, as pointed out by Betty Rollin, neither are they afraid of their doctors. They are perfectly willing to disagree and even change physicians if they are dissatisfied. One young woman bluntly says, "Hey, today we're consumers of medicine. We don't like the service, we go elsewhere! We don't have to put up with arrogance in our doctors. There is a surplus today."

As we have seen, at least one study suggests that it is the feisty, aggressive, determined, even sometimes disagreeable patient who survives cancer the longest. Not many of the volunteers are disagreeable, but many are feisty. They are not easy to manipulate or dictate to.

Many are like Dr. Rawlings. Now in his seventies, he developed an adenocarcinoma of the rectum. He was advised to have surgery immediately. But at his age such a serious procedure had a high rate of mortality. In addition, he says, "It leaves one with the problem of a colostomy, which some people handle very, very well, and others find, uh, very detrimental to their *joie de vivre.*" He decided to seek a second opinion. The second doctor told him of an alternative therapy being practiced by a radiation oncologist in Rochester, New York. If the cancer were not too far advanced and if it were in just the right location, this doctor could treat the lesion with intracavitary radiation. That is to say, a specially designed tube could be inserted into the rectum and radiation applied to the tumor. The sick physician flew to Rochester, underwent that treatment and recovered without a colostomy being necessary.

Speaking of the oncologist who treated him and spared him a colostomy, he says with a wry smile, "He had some fifty or sixty patients, the majority physicians, from all over the United States and some from outside the country." Asked why so many of the patients were physicians, he laughs heartily and says, "I'll let you make your own conclusion. I suppose there are many reasons why the procedure is not well known. One tends to practice what he has been trained to do. If you're a colo-rectal surgeon, you do colo-rectal surgery."

He laughs again, and adds,

> The same physician who told me of this option subsequently said he thought I was arrogant! But I didn't think it was arrogant to question some of the things that he and others were doing. I

wanted to know about them. I am very fond of this gentleman, and I don't want him to think I am arrogant. I'm just a little skeptical, and that has been my training through forty or fifty years.

But if the experience of cancer itself can lead to a more beautiful life, so can the experience of being a CanSurmount volunteer. It may have occurred to the reader to ask why anyone who had survived the horror of cancer and then found a new and immensely enriched life should go back to that world of sickness and fear and death. There are some doctors who question if it is good for their patients to serve in this way. Some even prefer that their patients do not become volunteers. One older physician shakes his head and says,

Most of the patients who refuse to become volunteers, or who quit, when I ask "Why?" say, "Well, I'm cured, and I don't want the fact that I've had cancer, or that I might have some risk of recurrence, continually stuffed down my neck. I just want to forget it. I don't want it to be part of my living." I think that is healthy.

But that doctor has not understood a deeper truth that the volunteer has learned well. John Burgess, whose wife is also a volunteer, says,

When we visit patients, we don't go only to listen. In a way it's therapy for us too. There are times when I have to force myself to go to that hospital. But I will come home, *we* will come home, exhausted. Totally drained. Yet it is a renewer. In the morning, when I've slept it off, it's as though I've grown inside a little bit.

Andy Bryant tells this story:

The most interesting patient I saw was one I didn't want to see. Poor guy from an Indian reservation in Montana. He was a quadruple amputee, no legs at all, and I don't think any arms. Certainly no hands. But he had cancer. I would have given a hundred dollars not to walk in that door. But I did, and it was the best thing that ever happened to me. I stopped feeling sorry for myself. As I remember, he had a lot of problems with his family. That was the most rewarding call I ever made.

Kay Borvansky eloquently expressed what the volunteers get out of the experience.

> I have gone high on life so many times I can't tell you. I have seen people sit and cry together . . . I mean, I've seen eight people, and one will start crying because she has just had some bad news, and the rest of us go right in with her. I feel like I've just been given a gift! For when I can hold somebody's hand and make them feel a little better, I can't tell you what a shot in the arm it is for me. At times I will just jump up and put my arms around someone while they cry. For some reason I get a tremendous inner strength out of that.

Dorothy Kubitchek says, "Part of the reason you visit cancer patients is that you want to keep in contact with THE IDEA. If you don't do something, the initial intensity weakens, the further you get away from cancer." The CanSurmount volunteer has found one of life's deepest secrets: to keep something very beautiful, one must give it away.

Shirley Jenkins, who has already been quoted, is one of the best examples of this. A young mother, only twenty-eight when she found she had chronic granulocytic leukemia, she was crushed by the news. Fortunately, she went into remission almost immediately, but the depression remained. Her husband, Don, tried unsuccessfully to bring her out of it. Finally, she went to see her pastor, a wise man who gave her a stiff talk. Shirley says, "He turned me around to the point where I started living instead of dying. I decided to go for it."

Paul sensed the change in his young patient and asked her to work as a volunteer with CanSurmount. She was a shy country girl who had grown up on a farm in Virginia, and the thought of talking to others, not to speak of spending so much time with other cancer patients, terrified her. Tentatively, she attended a meeting as an observer. Then she began to make calls. Difficult as it was for her, she found herself growing more confident by the day. Finally, she became so effective that Paul began asking her to speak to groups wanting to learn about CanSurmount. She says that was more terrifying than finding that she had leukemia. But today Shirley is a vibrant, cheerful, articulate leader and a coordinator at

Presbyterian Medical Center. She still has leukemia, but Shirley has so risen above it that few would even suspect it. Through her service to others she has retained the secret that cancer patients learn. She epitomizes what Jesus meant when he said, "Give, and it will be given to you. Good measure, pressed down, shaken together, running over, will he put into your lap."

# 11
# "I'm A Patient, Too"

There is a long road ahead before a cure for cancer can be found. Certainly, progress has been made, but cancer still ends in death more times than not. In an article in *Science 84*, Dr. Haydn Bush, director of the London Regional Cancer Centre in Canada, says acidly:

> Public misunderstanding about the differences in curability and the definitions of cure may have resulted in therapeutic claims that are at best inaccurate and at worst positively misleading.

For decades the public has been told by tabloids and even some responsible newspapers that science is on the verge of a cure for this disease. When it was shown that some cancers in animals were caused by virus, many thought it would be only a short time before the virus which caused human cancers would be discovered and a vaccine developed. Americans fantasized that children would soon line up for shots for cancer as they have for polio or whooping cough. But decades have passed, and it has still not been proven that any human cancers are caused by a virus. It now seems likely that many things can cause cancer, from tobacco smoke to virus to environmental pollutants.

The National Cancer Institute's program of testing hundreds and even thousands of chemicals for anti-cancer activity has not been spectacularly successful. Nor has the world wide search for a "magic bullet" which will destroy cancer cells while leaving normal tissue undamaged. Cancer continues to resist solution.

Which brings us back to where we began. Cancer patients need help—lots of it. And, for whatever reason one wants to accept, modern medicine is not providing it. Medicine is so committed to high technology that it seems to have little interest in personal care. For many diseases, mechanical medicine provides a quick cure and a speedy return to full health. When that is the outcome, everyone is happy. The patient may not miss the human touch. In fact, he may even prefer quick, impersonal treatment.

But when the illness is life-threatening, like cancer, the physician's lack of concern can be deeply disturbing. In dealing with such illness, the doctor finds himself in the same position his predecessors were fifty years ago: he is able to diagnose and describe the progress of the disease, but unable to do much about it. More is needed than a quick shot of penicillin or a prescription for a tranquilizer. The physician must regain the *art of healing.* And for that, recent graduates of medical school are poorly equipped. Lewis Thomas describes what the "healer" of the past had, and what the modern physician must re-learn.

> Most of the men who practiced this laying on of hands must have possessed, to begin with, the gift of affection. There are, certainly, some people who do not like other people much, and they would have been likely to stay away from an occupation requiring touching.

The day may come when we can go to a doctor to have a cancer treated as much as we now go to a garage for a new muffler. We deliver the automobile, pace the floor, glance impatiently at our watches while the necessary repairs are made. The day may yet arrive when we will inform the doctor that we have a little cancer and would he please treat it in a hurry since we have a two o'clock appointment. Under such circumstances, real rapport between doctor and patient is not crucial. But that day is far in the future. Cancer patients still need "the warm, reassuring touch," from one who has the "gift of affection."

There is little glory in providing care for suffering people. Nobel prizes in medicine are awarded for finding cures or isolating a new hormone or developing machines, not for giving kindness and understanding. Tax dollars and grants from cancer organizations find their way more readily into research than into care.

Ordering an injection of antibiotics is not emotionally demanding on a physician. Talking to a dying or terrified patient is, especially when the physician can do little else to help. It is also time consuming. Furthermore, the physician can charge more for high tech medicine than he can for human warmth. It is really no mystery why medical care has come to the point it has.

But whether or not the physician *wants* to be more caring of his seriously ill patients, the time has come when he *must*. He can no longer leave it to others to handle the "emotional stuff." Things are changing again in medicine. For perhaps the first time in history there is, at least in urban areas, a surplus of doctors. In the bluntest of terms, it is a "buyer's market." In fact, there is a growing movement with an emphasis on "patients' rights." Consumers who do not like the way they have been treated can easily find a physician more to their liking. And they are doing just that. If there has been a revolution in medical science, there is also one developing in medical consumerism. Because the media keep up a constant barrage of information about the latest in preventive medicine and medical technology, people know more than ever before. And the doctor is losing his godlike status in direct proportion to how much the consumer knows. For the first time in memory there is brisk competition for patients, and that competition is likely to intensify over the coming years.

But it is not a one-sided issue. Often patients expect too much from physicians. However much he may care, the physician today does not have in his black bag a magic pill to cure every disease. And not every doctor who is a fine physician, even a feeling one, can easily express his concern. Patients who sue doctors for failure to be gods who can make youth reappear or a knee straighten are hurting themselves and other consumers of medical care. They are driving the doctor into a corner where he may look at a patient as a potential adversary instead of seeing him as a person he wants to help. As the physician needs to be more understanding and caring, so do many patients.

Enter CanSurmount.

PAUL HAMILTON: The image I have of CanSurmount is that it is a catalyst for the development of a therapeutic community, made up of health professionals, the patients, and the families. I have learned so much from listening to the volunteers! Particularly volunteers who are my patients. They feel more comfortable talking with me about themselves, about other patients, and about family members. And I feel more comfortable listening to them.

They are peers in a sense, and I have encouraged that because it's healthy.

Encouraging communication between members of the therapeutic community is critical. Relaying to the physician a patient's real concerns, helping the patient understand his doctor's problems and limitations, sharing the volunteer's own first hand experience with both are important contributions.

The emotional pressures on a doctor, particularly one who deals constantly with very sick patients, are enormous. To suffer the rage of a patient, directed at the doctor who bears the bad news rather than at the disease, is exceedingly difficult. To answer such inevitable questions as, "How long will I live?" or, "How can I tell my children?" is enough to turn anyone's hair gray. Here the volunteer, who has had to deal with those very questions, can be of help. Paul Hamilton confesses that one of the reasons he began CanSurmount was to help him deal with his own loneliness and helplessness. By making patients, family members and volunteers part of the team, his burden is lessened.

There is an even more important service the volunteer can perform, one which many physicians will be unwilling to accept. The volunteer can *teach* the doctor. He can teach him what it is like to be a patient. He can help the doctor understand what fear is, how hard it is to win the prize of courage. When Paul Hamilton said that he had "learned so much," he did not mean tips on how to "manage" the cancer patient's care. He meant he had learned what it is like to be a human being going through the searing experience of having and being treated for cancer. By *listening* to patients, especially such mature and intelligent ones as those typical of CanSurmount volunteers, the doctor can come to *feel*, vicariously, the pain they feel. If the doctor takes his hand off the doorknob and listens, if he lets his patients weep in his presence, if he "dares to be vulnerable," he will learn an ancient truth which centuries of doctors knew very well: pain does not *harm* us. It causes discomfort; but it only harms us if we let it. If we summon up the courage necessary to endure pain, we grow.

And he will discover something else.

Dr. Paul Rosch, an expert in physician/patient communications, says:

Any doctor who remembers to treat the whole patient, not just his or her illness, is a doctor whom patients will revere. Many times it is more important to know what kind of patient has the disease than to know what kind of disease the patient has. In the final analysis, the secret to being a respected doctor is in truly caring for your patients—and showing it.

If the modern physician feels he should be admired and loved because he is able to inject penicillin developed by someone else, or because he can run exotic machines designed by others, or because he knows a great deal about the human body, he will be disappointed. He will not receive great admiration because of his learning. Many people are learned—lawyers, engineers, mathematicians, chemists, businessmen, professors, clergy, military officers, veterinarians, statesmen. . . . The list is endless. And each learned person, whatever the specialty, is eager to instruct the public in just how much respect he deserves. It was not learning which earned the physician of the past respect. He was an admirable human being because he participated in the pain and struggle of his patients. To paraphrase Dr. Peck, he was a great man because he had a great capacity for suffering.

This is, of course, asking a lot of the physician. But is it asking more than we ask of everyone? We want the insurance adjustor to sympathize with us, make a real effort to understand our peculiar circumstances. We want the military commander to sell the lives of our young soldiers dearly. We want our politicians to look out for the elderly and the helpless. We want the police to make a genuine effort to catch our assailant. We want our counselor to care about our marital problems.

In short, what we all want is for human beings to be fully human with each other. Anything less leaves us scarred.

It may be more difficult for a physician than for some. For physicians deal with heart-rending situations. Their potential for suffering is great. But one can only repeat what the cancer patient quoted earlier said, "If they can't stand the heat, get out of the kitchen." Or take this conversation between two volunteers:

*FIRST VOLUNTEER:* "Doctors have to keep their patients at a distance. You don't want to become a close friend of someone you think is going to die."

*SECOND VOLUNTEER:* "Why? We do it all the time. Even

though it scares the hell out of us. And we don't even get paid for it."

For young interns or residents this is stiff advice. To be thrown into a hospital setting where they are constantly with extremely sick and dying patients can be overwhelming. They can be forgiven if they falter under the burden and "decathect." But if they are to become healers, they must go beyond that immature adjustment. They must suffer with the patient, for only then will they grow. They must become like the CanSurmount volunteer who returns to the scene of his own pain and finds new strength in doing it. They will find that the increased maturity is worth the pain. And they will win the respect and admiration of their patients.

In its first ten years CanSurmount has helped myriads of patients and family members, and has won the support of many members of the medical community.

Dr. Eduardo R. Pajon, Jr.:

As a physician who specializes in oncology, it is certainly my goal to provide not only the best physical care, but also the best *emotional* care to my patients. Cancer patients, like many chronically ill patients, have special emotional needs that cannot be met by the physician alone.

One member of the multi-disciplinary team who can help the physician deal with these special emotional needs is the CanSurmount volunteer. For those of you who are not familiar with this organization let me explain . . . [that] what is so unique about this program is that the volunteers themselves have or have had cancer. I truly believe that unless one has been through the experience of having cancer, or has lost a loved one to cancer, there is no possible way we can know the devastation these people go through. We can sympathize, or empathize, but not having actually lost our hair, vomited through the night after a treatment, had stomatitis so badly we couldn't eat for a week, or faced our own mortality, it is impossible to know what our patients really go through.

The CanSurmount volunteer does know. He has been through it. He can relate to our patient on a different level. It is important for the patient to be able to talk to someone who's lived it and lived through it.

As physicians we are kidding ourselves if we think we can do it all. The CanSurmount volunteer offers us a means of giving support to our patients, another avenue in which to provide for the comprehensive care that we all strive for.

I strongly urge you to incorporate this program as part of your team approach to the cancer patient.

But there is still much to be done. Even support for CanSurmount may actually be an attempt, albeit unconscious, to avoid a responsibility that belongs to the medical community.

A young physician says:

I think that groups like CanSurmount do the job of giving emotional assurance to the patient better than any physician ever could. I hear it all the time, "My doctor should have shown more care and concern. My doctor should have helped me in this or that way." You can say that, but I think you're going to continue to say it for fifty years. It's not going to get any better. Groups like this are going to have to fill that void. It is beautiful that this is happening. People who have time to talk to people and who have the empathy and the concern. I applaud groups like CanSurmount, Alcoholics Anonymous, self-help groups that are out there helping other people with something they have gone through. Filling a need that everybody seems to feel that medicine should fill, but medicine isn't going to do it.

CanSurmount was designed to complement the role of the professional, not be a substitute for it. The CanSurmount "conspiracy" will not have been successful until it has brought about a revolution within the health care professions. The challenge is not to give up any of the wonderful advances of high tech medicine, but to recognize that medicine is still and will always be human beings working to help other human beings. CanSurmount will not have achieved its ends until the doctor and the nurse and everyone associated with medicine can say genuinely, "I am— vicariously, at least—a patient, too."

# Appendix

## How to Start Your Own CanSurmount Program

If you find that there is no CanSurmount group in your area, call the local headquarters of the American Cancer Society. They are listed below. Ask the division to establish a group. If they decline, start a group yourself. You will have to give it a different name, since the American Cancer Society has a copyright on "CanSurmount." But who cares what it is called? The important thing is that the people who need help receive it.

Whether you are beginning an official group for the American Cancer Society or starting one with a different name, roughly the same procedure should be followed.

1. Send to the American Cancer Society for information on the policies and procedures of the groups. Reading what others have done will save you having to re-invent the wheel.

2. Look around for other patients who would like to be volunteer callers. Don't be discouraged if some aren't interested. People generally have to feel good about themselves, and feel free to talk about their encounter with cancer before they can handle volunteer calling. Many former patients are too busy to spare the time. Just keep trying. Experience proves you'll eventually find plenty of people who are willing and able to help.

3. After you've lined up some volunteers sit down and talk over the policies and procedures recommended in the American Cancer Society materials. Give everyone a copy. It may also be helpful to have each person read this book.

4. Discuss which doctors and nurses you will invite to be advisors. You will need their cooperation to get into a hospital. Usually, it is best to seek the guidance and assistance of a medical oncologist, although an internist or radiation therapist can also be helpful. Surgeons are often less willing to become advisors, for the reasons discussed in this book.

153

5. Visit the doctor you have selected. Give him or her a copy of this book and also the materials from the American Cancer Society. Set up a time when your advisor can meet the other volunteers.

6. At the meeting decide on an approach to the hospital in which you want to make your first calls. It is helpful if the doctor and nurses who are acting as your advisors arrange an appointment and go with you to present your plan to the hospital administrator.

In general, it is better for a program to be hospital-based. Some, particularly in small towns, are based in the community or in a church. But it is easier if you operate out of a hospital and are accepted by the staff. In a hospital refuses to cooperate, you have no alternative but to work independently, calling only on patients who have returned to their homes.

7. Begin your calls. Start by visiting patients of your advisor, and remember to discuss every call with the other volunteers and with the physician. You'll quickly learn how to act and what to say.

8. After some experience and success, expand your work. Approach other physicians about calling on their patients. Ask additional hospitals to become involved.

9. Be on the constant lookout for people who will make good volunteers. Discuss those you're considering with current volunteers. If they agree with your judgment, set up training sessions to share the things you've learned with the new people.

You're on your way. Try to avoid a few of the pitfalls that can wreck your entire program:

1. Do not make any suggestions or express an opinion about the kind of treatment a patient is receiving. Leave that to the physician.

2. Be careful in your choice of volunteers. Some unstable persons or those with an ax to grind can cause trouble.

3. Remember not to talk about patients and their problems except to their physicians and other responsible people. What you will learn will be interesting, but it's also confidential. Treat it that way.

4. Act with a little dignity. Don't gush or be frivolous. These are sick people and they may not appreciate you're being sweetsie or cutesy. In the best sense of the word, be a little "professional."

5. But don't ever be pompous! Remember, being a good volunteer is being a friend who cares.

Once you've got a vital, strong program going, ask the hospital to provide an office and funds for a full time coordinator. That helps so much.

Good luck!

P. S. If you really run into insuperable obstacles, you can write Dr. Paul K. Hamilton, Jr. His address is 1721 East 19th Street, Denver, CO 80209. If you're desperate, you can even give him a call. His number is 303-860-8828.

# How to Contact CanSurmount

CanSurmoumt is a living organization, and as such is growing and changing almost every day. About half the states already have formally-instituted CanSurmount programs. Many other states were in the process of setting up CanSurmount groups as this book went to press. Listed below are the addresses and phone numbers of the chartered divisions of the American Cancer Society, listed by state, and (in some cases) state regional offices. (Canadian Cancer Society offices follow this list.) Contact these offices for the most current information about CanSurmount chapters near you. They will be glad to help.

ican Cancer Society
ma Division, Inc.
ffice Park Drive Suite 300
ngham, Alabama 35223
879-2242

can Cancer Society
 Division, Inc.
G Street
rage, Alaska 99501
277-8696

can Cancer Society
a Division, Inc.
'est Indian School Road
ox 33187
ix, Arizona 85067
234-3266

can Cancer Society
as Division, Inc.
West Markham Street
ox 3822
Rock, Arkansas 72203
564-3480-1-2

can Cancer Society
rnia Division, Inc.
Webster Street
ox 2061
ad, California 94604
393-7900

can Cancer Society
iego Unit
an Diego Ave., B-150
ego, CA 92110
299-4200

can Cancer Society
do Division, Inc.
outh Oneida
ox 24669
, Colorado 80224
58-2030

American Cancer Society
Presbyterian Medical Center
CanSurmount Office
1719 E. 19th Ave.
Dawson Hall, Room 216
Denver, CO 80219
(303) 839-6115

American Cancer Society
Connecticut Division, Inc.
Barnes Park South
14 Village Lane, P.O. Box 410
Wallingford, Connecticut 06492
(203) 265-7161

American Cancer Society
Delaware Division, Inc.
1708 Lovering Avenue, Suite 202
Wilmington, Delaware 19806
(302) 654-6267

American Cancer Society
District of Columbia Division, Inc.
Universal Building, South
1825 Connecticut Avenue, N.W.
Washington, D.C. 20009
(202) 483-2600

American Cancer Society
Florida Division, Inc.
1001 South MacDill Avenue
Tampa, Florida 33609
(813) 253-0541

American Cancer Society
Georgia Division, Inc.
1422 W. Peachtree Street, N.W.
Atlanta, Georgia 30309
(404) 892-0026

American Cancer Society
Hawaii Pacific Division, Inc.
Community Services Center Bldg.
200 North Vineyard Boulevard
Honolulu, Hawaii 96817
(808) 531-1662-3-4-5

American Cancer Society
Idaho Division, Inc.
1609 Abbs Street
P.O. Box 5386
Boise, Idaho 83705
(208) 343-4609

American Cancer Society
Illinois Division, Inc.
37 South Wabash Avenue
Chicago, Illinois 60603
(312) 372-0472

American Cancer Society
CanSurmount Program
Indiana Division, Inc.
9575 N. Valparaiso
Indianapolis, Indiana 46268
(317) 872-4432

American Cancer Society
Iowa Division, Inc.
Highway #18 West
P.O. Box 980
Mason City, Iowa 50401
(515) 423-0712

Pat Meier, Coordinator
St. Luke's Hospital
1026 A Avenue, N.E.
Cedar Rapids, IA 52402
(319) 369-7211

Pat Ouverson
Medical Affairs Director
American Cancer Society
Iowa Division, Inc.
Box 65710
West Des Moines, IA 50265-0710
(515) 253-0147

American Cancer Society
Kansas Division, Inc.
3003 Van Buren Street
Topeka, Kansas 66611
(913) 267-0131

American Cancer Society
Kentucky Division, Inc.
Medical Arts Bldg.
1169 Eastern Parkway
Louisville, Kentucky 40217
(502) 459-1867

American Cancer Society
Louisiana Division, Inc.
Masonic Temple Bldg., 7th Floor
333 St. Charles Avenue
New Orleans, Louisiana 70130
(504) 523-2029

American Cancer Society
Maine Division, Inc.
Federal and Green Streets
Brunswick, Maine 04011
(207) 729-3339

American Cancer Society
Maryland Division, Inc.
1840 York Rd., Suite K-M
P.O. Box 544
Timonium, Maryland 21093
(301) 561-4790

American Cancer Society
Massachusetts Division, Inc.
247 Commonwealth Avenue
Boston, Massachusetts 02116
(617) 267-2650

American Cancer Society
Michigan Division, Inc.
1205 East Saginaw Street
Lansing, Michigan 48906
(517) 371-2920

American Cancer Society
Michigan Division, Inc.
Muskegon Unit
1706 Clinton Street
Muskegon, MI 49442

American Cancer Society
Michigan Division, Inc.
Ottawa Unit
563 College Ave.
Holland, MI 49423

American Cancer Society
Minnesota Division, Inc.
3316 West 66th Street
Minneapolis, Minnesota 55435
(612) 925-2772

CanSurmount Coordinator
American Cancer Society
Hennepin County Unit
3316 West 66th Street
Minneapolis, MN 55435

American Cancer Society
Ramsey County Unit
2233 University Avenue
Suite 320
St. Paul, MN 55114

CanSurmount Coordinator
American Cancer Society
Duluth Unit
600 West Superior Street
Duluth, MN 55802

American Cancer Society
Mississippi Division, Inc.
345 North Mart Plaza
Jackson, Mississippi 39206
(601) 362-8874

American Cancer Society
Missouri Division, Inc.
3322 American Avenue
P.O. Box 1066
Jefferson City, Missouri 65102
(314) 893-4800

CanSurmount Group
Lester E. Cox Medical Center
1423 N. Jefferson Street
Springfield, Missouri 65802

CanSurmount Program
Barnes Hospital
Barnes Hospital Plaza
St. Louis, Missouri 63110

Charles E. Still Hospital
1125 South Madison Street
P.O. Box 1128
Jefferson City, MO 65101

American Cancer Society
Montana Division, Inc.
2820 First Avenue South
Billings, Montana 59101
(406) 252-7111

American Cancer Society
Nebraska Division, Inc.
8502 West Center Road
Omaha, Nebraska 68124
(402) 393-5800

American Cancer Society
Nevada Division, Inc.
1325 East Harmon
Las Vegas, Nevada 89109
(702) 798-6877

American Cancer Society
New Hampshire Division, Inc.
686 Mast Road
Manchester, New Hampshire 03102
(603) 669-3270

American Cancer Society
New Jersey Division, Inc.
CN2201, 2600 Route 1
North Brunswick, New Jersey ▪
(201) 297-8000

American Cancer Society
New Mexico Division, Inc.
5800 Lomas Blvd., N.E.
Albuquerque, New Mexico 87▮
(505) 262-2336

American Cancer Society
New York State Division, Inc.
6725 Lyons Street, P.O. Box 7
East Syracuse, New York 1305▮
(315) 437-7025

American Cancer Society
Long Island Division, Inc.
535 Broad Hollow Road
(Route 110)
Melville, New York 11747
(516) 420-1111

American Cancer Society
New York City Division, Inc.
19 West 56th Street
New York, New York 10019
(212) 586-8700

American Cancer Society
Queens Division, Inc.
112-25 Queens Boulevard
Forest Hills, New York 1137▮
(718) 263-2224

American Cancer Society
Westchester Division, Inc.
901 North Broadway
White Plains, New York 106▮
(914) 949-4800

American Cancer Society
North Carolina Division, Inc.
11 South Boylan Avenue
Suite 221
Raleigh, North Carolina 27603
(919) 834-8463

American Cancer Society
North Dakota Division, Inc.
Hotel Graver Annex Bldg.
115 Roberts Street
P.O. Box 426
Fargo, North Dakota 58102
(701) 232-1385

American Cancer Society
Ohio Division, Inc.
1375 Euclid Avenue
Suite 312
Cleveland, Ohio 44115
(216) 771-6700

erican Cancer Society
lahoma Division, Inc.
0 North Cromwell
lahoma City, Oklahoma 73112
5) 946-5000

erican Cancer Society
gon Division, Inc.
0 S.W. Curry
tland, Oregon 97201
3) 295-6422

American Cancer Society
241 Commercial
Salem, Oregon 97201

American Cancer Society
1412 Pearl Street
Eugene, Oregon 97401

American Cancer Society
125 S. Central
Medford, Oregon 97501

American Cancer Society
1012 N.W. Wall, # 203
Bend, Oregon 97708

American Cancer Society
920 S.W. Frazer
Pendleton, Oregon 97801

erican Cancer Society
nsylvania Division, Inc.
ute 422 & Sipe Avenue
. Box 416
rshey, Pennsylvania 17033
7) 533-6144

American Cancer Society
Philadelphia Division, Inc.
1422 Chestnut Street
Philadelphia, Pennsylvania 19102
(215) 665-2900

erican Cancer Society
rto Rico Division, Inc.
enue Domenech 273
o Rey, P.R.)
O Box 6004
Juan, Puerto Rico 00936
9) 764-2295

erican Cancer Society
de Island Division, Inc.
Blackstone Blvd.
idence, Rhode Island 02906
1) 831-6970

erican Cancer Society
th Carolina Division, Inc.
2 Devine Street
mbia, South Carolina 29205
) 256-0245

American Cancer Society
South Dakota Division, Inc.
1025 North Minnesota Avenue
Hillcrest Plaza
Sioux Falls, South Dakota 57104
(605) 336-0897

American Cancer Society
Tennessee Division, Inc.
713 Melpark Drive
Nashville, Tennessee 37204
(615) 383-1710

American Cancer Society
Texas Division, Inc.
3834 Spicewood Springs Road
P.O. Box 9863
Austin, Texas 78766
(512) 345-4560

American Cancer Society
Utah Division, Inc.
610 East South Temple
Salt Lake City, Utah 84102
(801) 322-0431

CanSurmount Coordinator
Weber County
American Cancer Society
First Security Bank Bldg. #218
2404 Washington Blvd.
Ogden, UT 84401
(801) 393-8657

CanSurmount Coordinator
Utah County
American Cancer Society
10 E. 300 North
Provo, UT 84601
(801) 373-5886

CanSurmount Coordinator
Davis County
American Cancer Society
11 North Main
Kaysville, UT 84037
(801) 544-5836

American Cancer Society
Vermont Division, Inc.
13 Loomis Street, Drawer C
Montpelier, Vermont 05602
(802) 223-2348

American Cancer Society
Virginia Division, Inc.
4240 Park Place Court
P.O. Box 1547
Glen Allen, Virginia 23060
(804) 270-0142

American Cancer Society
Washington Division, Inc.
2120 First Avenue North
Seattle, Washington 98109
(206) 283-1152

American Cancer Society
Southwest Area Office
515 South "M", #205
Tacoma, WA 98405
(206) 383-1663

American Cancer Society
Eastern Area Office
1717 NW Blvd.
Spokane, WA 99205
(509) 326-5802

American Cancer Society
West Virginia Division, Inc.
Suite 100
240 Capitol Street
Charleston, West Virginia 25301
(304) 344-3611

American Cancer Society
Wisconsin Division, Inc.
615 North Sherman Avenue
P.O. Box 8370
Madison, Wisconsin 53708
(608) 249-0487

American Cancer Society
Milwaukee Division, Inc.
11401 West Watertown Plank Road
Wauwatosa, Wisconsin 53226
(414) 453-4500

CanSurmount Program
La Crosse Lutheran Hospital
1910 South Avenue
La Crosse, WI 54601

CanSurmount Program
St. Joseph's Community Hospital
551 Silverbrook Drive
West Bend, WI 53095

American Cancer Society
Wyoming Division, Inc.
Indian Hills Center
506 Shoshoni
Cheyenne, Wyoming 82009
(307) 638-3331

# CANADIAN CANCER SOCIETY DIVISIONS

*British Columbia*
Canadian Cancer Society
955 West Broadway St.
Vancouver, B.C.
V5Z 3X8
Telephone: (604) 736–1211

*Alberta*
Canadian Cancer Society
Suite 310
2424 4th Street, S.W.
Calgary, Alberta
T2S 2T4
Telephone: (403) 228–4487

*Saskatchewan*
Canadian Cancer Society
2629 29th Avenue
Regina, Saskatchewan
S4S 2Y9
Telephone: (306) 584-1054

*Manitoba*
Canadian Cancer Society
193 Sherbrook
Winnipeg, Manitoba
R3C 2B7
Telephone: (204) 774-7483

*Ontario*
Canadian Cancer Society
1639 Yonge St.
Toronto, Ontario
M4T 2W6
Telephone: (416) 488-5400

*Quebec*
Canadian Cancer Society
550 Sherbrooke Street W.,
Suite 985
Montreal, P.Q.
H3A 3C5
(514) 842-3424

*New Brunswick*
Canadian Cancer Society
P.O. Box 2089
Saint John, New Brunswick
E2L 3T5
Telephone: (506) 652-7600

*Nova Scotia*
Canadian Cancer Society
201 Roy Building
1657 Barrington St.
Halifax, Nova Scotia
B3J 2A1
Telephone: (902) 423-6183

*Prince Edward Island*
Canadian Cancer Society
P.O. Box 115
131 Water Street
2nd Floor
Charlottetown, P.E.I.
C1A 1A8
Telephone: (902) 566-4007

*Newfoundland*
Canadian Cancer Society
34 Pippy Place
P.O. Box 8921
St. Johns's, Newfoundland
A1B 3R9
Telephone: (709) 753-6520